SOMATIC EXERCISES

FOR NERVOUS SYSTEM REGULATION

35 Beginner – Intermediate Techniques
To Reduce Anxiety & Tone Your Vagus Nerve In
Under 10 Minutes A Day

This Is Really Important.
It's a Sincere Thank You.

My name is Wayne, the founder of LearnWell.

My Dad put a book in my hands when I was 13. It was written by Zig Ziglar and it changed the course of my life. Since then, it's been books that have helped me get over breakups, learn how to be a good friend, study the lives of good people and books have been the source of my persistence through some pretty challenging times.

My purpose is now to return the favor. To create books that might be the turning point in the lives of people around the world, just like they've been for me. It's enough to almost bring me to tears to think of you holding this book, seeking information and wisdom from something that I've helped to create. I'm moved in a way that I can't fully explain.

We're a small and 'beyond-enthusiastic' team here at LearnWell. We're writers, editors, researchers, designers, formatters (oh ... and a bookkeeper!) who take your decision to learn with us incredibly seriously. We consider it a privilege to be part of your learning journey. Thank you for allowing us to join you.

If there's anything we did really well, anything we messed up, or anything AT ALL that we could do better, would you please write to us and tell us (like, right now!) We would love to hear from you!

readers@learnwellbooks.com

We're sending you our thanks, our love and our very best wishes.

Wayne

and the team at LearnWell Books.

LearnWell Books

At LearnWell, we think learning is the most important thing a person can do. Learners grow, lead, and solve important problems. We consider it a privilege that you've chosen one of our books to learn from.

In return, we have invested significant effort in creating what we believe are the best books in the world, on the topics we choose to write about.

Your books come with several complementary features, including:

WORKBOOK

Accompanying these two books is a comprehensive Workbook that will enhance your learning and increase your knowledge retention.

Before reading, please get your copy of the Workbook here:

www.learnwellbooks.com/embody

It contains exercises that match the content of each chapter. It's interactive, user-friendly and proven to be the best way to absorb the valuable information in this book.

EMAIL LEARNING COURSE

As we write our books, we conduct enormous amounts of research. Not all of what we discover ends up in the books but some of this information is highly relevant and deserves to be shared. So, our writers capture these interesting 'side-notes' in a series of short emails. These messages become like a private tutorial. Similar to having the writer sitting with you as you read, sharing their thoughts and insights.

If you choose to get the Workbook, you will also be entitled to receive this online tutorial, at no charge.

I wrote this for you.

You deserve to feel good.

CONTENTS

WORKBOOK

The average reader remembers just 14% of what they read. To dramatically enhance the amount of knowledge you absorb on this important topic, we have produced a user-friendly Workbook that follows the content of this book, chapter by chapter. Before beginning this book, make sure you receive a copy of your Workbook. Follow the link below:

Get Access To Your Free Workbook Here:

www.learnwellbooks.com/embody

INTRODUCTION

The thought of therapy most likely brings to mind hours upon hours of talking where topics range from mundane to past trauma wound reopening.

The treatment for physical trauma is much the same – revisiting, medicating, and leaving the doctor's office feeling stuck with your burdens.

While many popular healing modalities have a purpose and a place, very few are able to approach trauma healing in a holistic, self-empowering way. A lot of chronic trauma sufferers, including those of us with chronic mental health ailments, have felt the powerlessness that comes from seeing doctors over and over again with little or sometimes no progress toward healing.

Before I learned about somatic exercise, I had already taken my healing into my own hands. However, upon facing mental health challenges that manifested in a very real and physical way, I was forced to try something new. I could no longer get away with intellectualizing my trauma. I had to stop and let myself feel.

Now, years after that unexpected hospital visit, somatics have changed my life. I have gained a sense of safety within my body that is becoming increasingly easy to return to after stress. All I can wish for is that sharing what I've learned can help change your life, too.

You don't need to be or see a professional somatic practitioner to experience big progress, either. The exercises in this book are some of the most widely used and effective somatic exercises, regardless of your experience level.

I've split the information into 6 simple chapters, 4 of which hold all the basic information you need on somatics to understand why it works and how you can get started. The final 2 chapters are all about the exercises, with Chapter 5 acting as a vault for the 35 somatic exercises you will learn. As for Chapter 6, this is where you create your own personalized 10-minute somatic exercise program that you can complete every day for life-changing results.

I'm so eager to share this information with you. Somatic practice is truly a breakthrough healing modality, proving just how important the mind-body connection is in both physical and mental trauma cases. However, even without trauma, somatic practice is a powerful tool in regulating emotions and building self-awareness. A nervous system in harmony can improve your life, regardless of your struggles.

Humans will never be void of stress. That's what our nervous systems were built to protect us from. But with modern lifestyles, our nervous systems have adapted to cope in a dysregulated state of chronic survival mode.

It doesn't have to be that way.

With a quick 10-minute daily somatic practice, we can train the nervous system to regulate and return to harmony after stress. If you're ready to learn a skill that will carry you through all of life's burdens in an empowering and productive way, keep reading. Join me in Chapter 1, where we will start this journey off at the deep end of all the incredible benefits of somatic practice.

THE WISDOM & BENEFITS OF SOMATIC PRACTICES

Creating Physical And Mental Well-Being Through The Power Of The Body-Mind Connection

"There's no question that the mind-body connection is real, even if we can't quantify it. Hope is one of the greatest weapons we have to fight disease."

– David Agus

The gnawing feeling in my stomach had transformed into nausea, the slight imbalance in my stature became sways of rocking dizziness, and the spiraling thoughts in my head twisted into a slew of confusion as my body went into a shivering shock. I picked up the phone and called my partner for help. This was a medical emergency.

By the time he arrived, my legs had given way beneath me. The blurry reality around me blurred into blackness as I cried out, "I'm not ready to die!" I couldn't believe my life was over at the young age of 26. There was pain for a moment and then numbness. But things then took an unexpected turn.

I felt my partner's arms carrying me to the vehicle, and my blurry vision returned. The cool air of the air conditioner caressed my cheek as relief that I was still breathing washed over me. We arrived at the emergency department.

By the time a doctor came, I could walk, talk, and see normally. I insisted that there was something seriously wrong. However, multiple clear test results indicated that it was simply a severe panic attack.

This was beyond what I believed my mind was capable of.

Unfortunately, the panic attacks continued. But the cause of my panic seemed out of my mind's control. None of the techniques I'd known before seemed to work. It was as if the stress that I'd been under for some time had bundled up into a knot that continued to trigger my fight-or-flight response daily.

I couldn't escape it, trying to only made things worse. I had to accept and trust that this wasn't only a problem in my mind but in my body as well. So, after reading about a technique to soothe some nerve I'd never heard of before that was somehow connected to my fight-or-flight system, I decided to try it.

Knowing I would be alone for the next 15 minutes, I closed my eyes, sat up straight, and started humming. It was a deep hum that reverberated down my throat and across my chest. It didn't make any sense to me at the time how this simple exercise could actually do anything to help me, but I was so beaten down and lost that I was willing to try anything.

After releasing a deep, raw hum between each breath, I felt tears forming in the corners of my eyes. And then I laughed. A subtle sense of silliness washed over me, and the little touch of joy I felt was enough. I felt something other than numbness, worry, or panic, and I gripped onto it. If I could feel it for those few seconds after such an easy, seemingly silly exercise, then I could replicate that experience. "Maybe the joy could build, and I could feel like myself again," I thought.

It did.

After just a few months of expanding my efforts to understand and experience these exercises, I didn't just feel like my old self again. I felt better. I started to glow. The numbness transformed into a beautiful sensitivity and awareness. And on the days when I felt low or anxious, I could trust myself to work through those feelings and allow them. I made space for discomfort in my life, which inadvertently expanded into more inner safety, understanding, and joy. My digestive issues slowly resolved themselves, the daily vertigo I was experiencing subsided, and my physical energy levels improved significantly.

I didn't fully understand how or why these exercises worked, but my body didn't need me to understand. It simply needed me to allow it to *feel*. There were so many traumatic years in my life that I had worked through in my mind but never in my body. Every time I shoved an emotion down, smiled through the pain, and pretended I was fine, my body remembered. These exercises allowed me to sit quietly with my body and flip through the memories. They were all somatic exercises.

Almost any movement can be classified as a somatic exercise – even breathing. What defines it is the intention to release tension, stress, or trauma through movement. You naturally engage your mind-body connection when you use your body to release stress or trauma. This is the basis of somatic practice.

However, it's important to understand that bodies don't remember images or words as the mind does. It remembers physical sensations, emotions, and muscle tension. Taking the time to slowly release these "memories" through movement, breath, and other physical techniques allowed my body to lighten its traumatic load.

I'm excited to help deepen your understanding of somatic exercises because I know how effective they can be. I know how painful, confusing, and often scary it can be to feel chronically dysregulated. But I want you to know that becoming unstuck is possible. Somatic exercises are an easy addition to your healing journey that may very likely be the missing piece you've been waiting for – as they were for me.

For the rest of this chapter, I'd like to guide you through understanding these practices to further build your trust in them. I'll be touching on the interconnectedness of the mind and body, explaining the neurological systems these exercises work on, and how emotions impact the body. I will also unravel the importance of awareness for your mind-body relationship and what role that can play in an effective healing journey.

THE MIND-BODY CONNECTION

Your body and mind are intricately interconnected. It's difficult to affect the one without impacting the other in some way. When you are struggling with a physical illness or disease, the mind experiences changes, and vice versa. As a simple example, isn't it interesting how people with depression often feel physically fatigued or how low blood sugar can trigger anxiety? Our thoughts, emotions, and mental attitude can impact our physical health, and our physical health can influence how we feel.

In the same way, it's possible to heal physical symptoms with mental healing and mental symptoms with physical movement. The impact goes both ways. Somatic practices work with this mind-body connection to heal the mind by using the body while simultaneously improving physical health by releasing stored stress and trauma.

However, the mind-body connection is not a hypothetical concept. The mind and body are linked by a very important system of neuronal pathways known as the nervous system.

NEUROLOGICAL PATHWAYS

The human nervous system is the communication system that carries electrical signals between the body and the mind. It translates thoughts into actions and external stimuli into memory or mental experience. It comprises a complex system of neurons that spans the entire body and brain. That's why it has such a pivotal role in somatic practice. Regulating the nervous system is the core principle of somatics.

A regular somatic practice aims to improve our body awareness and muscle control to help encourage healthy communication between the body and the brain. It also aims to strengthen and balance the nervous system so that it can bounce back from stress quicker and with less negative impact on the body.

A nervous system that takes longer to regulate may produce uncomfortable fight-or-flight symptoms, inflammation, or other physiological changes for longer than necessary. However, a healthy one will allow faster recovery times if the body or the mind experiences significant stress or trauma. From sleep, movement, balance, and breathing to thoughts, emotions, perception, and neuroplasticity, the nervous system is connected to almost every aspect of well-being.[1]

With the branches of the nervous system connecting each of these bodily and mental processes, it makes sense that each of these processes can influence each other. One of the most impactful aspects of the mind-body connection is emotion. It is a powerful player within the healing game and is tightly woven into almost every aspect of life.

IMPACT OF EMOTIONS ON THE BODY

Emotions can have both a short-term and long-term impact on the body. In the short term, emotions often manifest various physical symptoms and sensations. Think about the last time you experienced conflict with someone and felt hurt or angry. How did your body feel?

Often, in these moments of heightened emotion, our nervous systems become activated, and symptoms such as a racing heart, increased body heat, sweating, and crying present themselves. It's also possible to experience an emotional shutdown, where we close ourselves off, suppress the emotions to avoid them, or protect ourselves from them, and other symptoms present themselves, such as numbness.

Suppressing or struggling to properly process big emotions can lead to a long-term emotional impact on the body. This is often when our bodies store these excess emotions in the form of tense muscles, weakened immune function, and chronic health issues. When we don't fully process emotions or trauma and instead carry them with us, it requires energy. Slowly, this extra weight of unprocessed baggage weighs our nervous systems down.

Think about a hot air balloon. Your body is the basket and balloon, while your mind is the passenger. The more you carry with you emotionally, the more you weigh the balloon down, making it harder to function. Somatic exercises can do two things: they can help you release emotions to lighten your load and enhance the working system of your balloon so it can function optimally. They don't just focus on one aspect of an interconnected system. They work to improve the entire system. And at the core of that system is awareness.

THE ROLE OF AWARENESS IN HEALING

By the time my chronic stress had triggered severe panic attacks, my nervous system was exhausted. I had ignored all the warning signs and continued to "push through," as many of us can relate to. It had become a habit to keep going despite the desperate internal calls to rest I was receiving from my nervous system.

Bouts of anxiety, derealization, nausea, vertigo, and more became symptoms I shrugged off and coped with to keep up with my jam-packed lifestyle and ignore the major stressors in my life at the time. Although I was an avid meditator before this point, I was too scared to sit still for a moment in my body and mind. I knew it would not be comfortable, so I avoided it.

In hindsight, while the panic attack caught me by surprise, there were warning signs for weeks, if not months before. My appetite had changed, I relied on daily intense exercise to take the edge off, I felt either tearful or numb on most days, and my evenings were filled with mindless social media scrolling or watching series I'd seen a hundred times before. I did little else to manage my stress because my time was limited, and I didn't believe there was much else I could do to change my circumstances at that point.

But there was one thing that could have turned things around much sooner: An awareness of my internal state.

The one thing I was avoiding most – feeling – was what would've, and eventually did, help me heal. Because emotions manifest themselves in bodily sensations, a sense of bodily awareness is paramount for addressing physical and mental discomfort.

Think about the last time you stubbed your toe. The pain lets you know that something in your body requires your attention and nurturing. Emotional pain is much the same. Think about the last time you had your heart broken or lost something important. How did it feel in your body? Did you feel a tinge of emotional pain?

An awareness of emotional pain and sensations allows you to identify where the emotion manifests in your body so you can better nurture and release it. Somatic exercises help to increase your mind-body awareness in this way.

ENHANCE MIND-BODY AWARENESS

Somatic exercises don't just accomplish one goal. While they work to engage and balance the nervous system, this can achieve many things. The intentional movements of somatics are designed to reshape neurological pathways in the nervous system to positively impact the mind-body connection. A strong mind-body connection can:

- Heighten your sensory perception
- Release muscle tension and stress
- Improve proprioception (sense of position) and balance
- Stabilize mood and thinking patterns
- Increase mindfulness and outlook

A strong mind-body connection is achieved through strong mind-body awareness. The more consistently you practice being in your body and paying attention to the sensations and experiences within it, the easier it is to notice positive and negative changes.

Noticing the changes and working to release or process stress as quickly as possible allows your nervous system to move on quicker, reducing the time you experience the negative symptoms associated with stress.

Somatic exercises encourage you to slow down and spend time in your body. They ask you to become aware of certain areas in your body, sensations, and other changes or processes so you can release and shift them. Rather than speaking about a stressor, avoiding uncomfortable emotions, or trying to release stress in a way that might do more damage at times, somatics requires you to feel your way through healing in a manageable and empowering way.

I love the expression: choose your hard. Pushing away my stress and avoiding my inner experience with distraction, exercise, and emotional suppression made things feel less painful in the moment but caused more problems in the long term. However, slowing down, going inward, and feeling the pain I knew I was experiencing deep down was harder in the moment but made things easier in the long term.

Choosing to practice somatic exercises is choosing a little bit of potential discomfort regularly to reduce significant discomfort in the long term. However, the best part about them is that they can feel extremely healing while often being the most relaxing and centered part of your day. Like stretching a stiff muscle, somatics always comes with a positive reward, even if that reward is simply a softer brow, an extra smile, or a moment of harmony between your mind and your body. When you're ready, turn to Chapter 2 and prepare yourself for the practical aspects of somatics you need to know before attempting the exercises.

MASTERING MOVEMENT FOR MIND-BODY HARMONY

Effective Techniques for Nervous System Harmony

"Much ill health is due to emotional congestion. Constant rythmical movement is necessary to health and harmony."

— Emmet Fox

Growing up, I often felt a little rough around the edges. While I tried my best to have a calm demeanor, inside, I was either a bit jittery or completely numb. Finding a middle ground of safety seemed far-fetched. My nervous system was more often than not in some form of fight-or-flight response. My trauma still ruled my life.

As I matured into a young woman, determined to overcome her depression and anxiety, mindfulness, meditation, and other regulating practices became a part of my daily routine. Even without understanding the full neurological impact, my health improved significantly – but not all the way.

Although many things can regulate the nervous system, having an active understanding of how can make all the difference. As awful as the panic attack in my late 20s was, it led me on a path of nervous system discovery. Knowing how to safely explore the sensations in my body and my thoughts created a sense of harmony between them. Rather than panicking at the first sign of discomfort, I could sit with it, acknowledge it, and respond to it.

Nervous system harmony is not about never feeling dysregulated or uncomfortable. It's about feeling empowered to respond to dysregulation. It's about finding balance within both regulated and dysregulated states. Knowing how somatic movement influences these states will allow you to start from a place of empowerment and understanding to navigate the experience in the most healing way.

CORE PRINCIPLES OF SOMATIC MOVEMENT

Somatic movement is a tool for building awareness and a tool of response. It can and should be used for all states of the nervous system. The more readily you can engage in a somatic movement in times of stress, the more effective it will be. This comes from practicing even when everything feels normal or good. The awareness you build allows you to better identify your unique stress response and take action quickly.

There are several core principles supporting somatic movement, each one touching on a different area of the nervous system:

- Mind-body connection: Somatic movements integrate the mind and the body by promoting a heightened awareness of your bodily sensations and movements to better understand your body's unique response to stimuli, stress, or emotions.

- Breath awareness: Intentional breathing is a foundational skill in somatic practice. It helps switch your nervous system response from fight-or-flight to 'rest and digest,' promoting relaxation and well-being.

- Mindful movement: The core movements of a somatic practice involve slow, intentional movements that promote a sense of focus and relaxation while building bodily awareness.

- Tension release: Stress and trauma, both physical and mental, may cause chronic muscle tension. Somatic movement is designed to target and release this tension in a physically and emotionally healing way.

- Neuroplasticity: The brain is an organ that can continue to heal and grow throughout our lives. Mindful somatic movement can rewire neural pathways to build a more balanced and regulated nervous system.

Because the nervous system spans the entire body, somatic movement works holistically to heal and harmonize each area of the body and mind. For example, if you have a tight and painful shoulder, it can help to release the pain, tension, and stress related to the problem.

The key to using somatic movement in a way that works best for you is picking exercises that target the most dysregulated areas of your nervous system. Your body sends signals to communicate what it needs. Your mind needs to acknowledge those signals so that you can respond as quickly and effectively as possible.

RECOGNIZING BODY SIGNALS

The nervous system is an intricate web whose corners reach the top of our heads and the tips of our toes and fingers. When something goes wrong somewhere along the web, our body sends a signal to our brain. This signal is a message with a lot of information, but it is often coded in physical sensations such as pain, tingling, temperature change, or other bodily changes.

Because of our mind-body connection, even a mental change can stimulate our bodies. Our bodies are the communicator that signals our minds about what's wrong. For example, if you watch a horror movie and feel the hairs on your neck stand up, that could be a signal that you're scared. Or, if you're taking a walk and suddenly feel pain in your right ankle, it's a signal that your ankle is overworked.

Whichever way your body chooses to communicate an emotion or problem, its signals are there for your attention. It's up to you to use those signals and respond to the important ones. For example, if your ankle starts to hurt while you're on a walk, you can recognize that signal and decide to take a break. Or if you hear a strange sound outside and your hair rises, you can get up and lock your doors.

Your response to your bodily signals is meant to remedy the dysregulation. But it's difficult to regulate dysregulation when you don't know what caused it or what it means. That's where an improved mind-body connection and awareness are so useful.

When you engage in a somatic exercise, it's important to:

- Close your eyes where possible.

- Allow your awareness to scan through your body.

- Pay attention to the areas that catch your awareness.

- Identify what or how you feel in those areas.

- Acknowledge the sensation.

- Allow the sensation to exist while responding.

- Choose how you will respond in a way that soothes that sensation rather than trying to escape it.

 In your Workbook, there is a space for you to try out this simple body scan exercise. When you're done, use a colored pen or marker to circle areas around the diagram where you felt a significant sensation. Draw a line to each area and make a note of how the sensation felt. Journal your experience and write down anything that stood out to you. Then, answer the questions for future reference.

Somatic movement and mind-body awareness allow you to recognize body signals with care and curiosity. When you can do this, it becomes easier to decode their meanings and respond in a restorative way. These movements are designed to release stress on their own, but your mind-body awareness allows you to adjust movements according to your unique needs.

GENTLE MOVEMENT FOR STRESS RELEASE

Somatic movements naturally release physical tension and reduce stress because of how they are practiced. Although they are often called exercises and involve careful intentional movement, they are not necessarily designed to increase your heart rate or strengthen your muscles.

Somatic movement is gentle.

Anyone can reap the benefits of this practice. They are intended to be slow, relaxing, and deliberate. They might incorporate gentle repetition of a single slow movement, holding specific body positions, intentionally softening muscles, or moving between positions in a slow and controlled way.

Taking the time each day to work through just 10 minutes of somatic movement can give your body and mind the intentional break they need to fully relax. These movements promote relaxation and effectively release physical tension by calming the nervous system.

A calm nervous system naturally reduces heart rate, blood pressure, muscle tension, and mental stress. It can safely enter the rest and digest state, where the mind-body connection can experience safety and relaxation. However, although these movements are designed to work regardless of your unique needs, you can modify any exercises to get the most out of them.

ADAPTIVE MOVEMENT STRATEGIES

You may suffer from a health condition or physical injury requiring you to modify your exercises. Rather than ruling great exercises out, you can adjust them to better fit your capabilities and needs.

Sometimes, only a modified exercise may improve your nervous system health by avoiding unnecessary strain on your body and better targeting problem areas. You can modify exercises by:

- Adjusting positions to maximize comfort and release.

- Reducing the range of motion the exercise asks for.

- Using supports or props like pillows, yoga blocks, or a chair.

- Progressing only when you're ready and able to.

- Taking additional time to rest in between movements.

- Modifying positions to accommodate physical conditions.

Examples of modified somatic exercises would include choosing to do an exercise from a seated position if standing is not comfortable, using a pillow to support your back during movements that require back stretches or lying down, only doing a movement halfway if the full range of motion is painful or not possible, taking your time to sit up slowly from a lying down position, and even changing or combining exercises to better suit your needs.

Somatic exercises are most effective when you work with your body to complete them. They are about listening to your body and knowing when you've reached your limit. Because these movements are designed to soften, stretch, and release tension in your muscles for nervous system harmony, it's important to understand your unique mental and physical needs.

Your body will have plenty of signals for you to identify and use to help you become more in tune with yourself. Remember to maintain awareness within your body before, during, and after somatic movements.

Building your mind-body awareness will allow you to recognize and respond to your needs quickly and effectively. This paves the way for nervous system balance and regulation as you learn not to ignore sensations but to see them for what they are: your body's communication system – its voice. Now that you understand the practical side of somatic exercises, please join me in Chapter 3, where we will explore the emotional impact of somatics.

NAVIGATING EMOTIONAL RELEASE
THROUGH SOMATIC MOVEMENT

How To Recognize And Release Emotions
To Build Emotional Resilience

"The oak fought the wind and was broken, the willow bent when it must and survived."

– Robert Jordan

The floor seemed to push up against my back, holding me in a sweet, relaxing surrender. I felt at peace for a moment as the tension along my spine, hips, and shoulders melted into it. This was a peace I was able to feel on many occasions since starting a daily somatic practice, but what came next was new for me.

In that bubble of safety, something long-hidden emerged. It was a strange swell of emotion – neither good nor bad – that seemed to wash over my entire body. A gentle release of tears began, and I allowed it. I decided not to resist the experience and simply let it fully surface. The release became cathartic.

The emotions that surfaced seemed to have come from somewhere beyond the present, somewhere that was still holding onto what should have been released ages ago. And when it was over, I felt as if I could sleep. As the heaviness of the emotion washed away, a beautiful, serene lightness replaced it. I opened my eyes and felt moved for a moment.

Emotions can become "trapped" in our bodies when we don't know how to fully process and release them. Difficult emotions often arrive, even daily, for some. Imagine what that can feel like in the body when those powerful, heavy emotions stay with us. How does it feel to carry them around? The strain on our nervous system is major.

Emotional release is a big part of somatic practice. For our nervous system to become balanced, it needs to even the scales. If it's holding onto a lot of heavy, trapped emotions, it quite literally holds onto them by increasing muscle tension, inflammation, and more.

But when you release that bodily tension, the scales need to even out again. That's when the nervous system can let go of stored emotions. It can no longer carry them if it wants to stay balanced. The only way for it to release trapped emotions is through the mind-body connection. It needs to flow *through* you.

This is when somatic practice can feel daunting, but I'd like to demystify the experience for you. In this chapter, I will explain how and why emotions may come up and how to safely and successfully move through the experience. Understanding the experience will allow you to deepen your practice without resistance.

UNDERSTANDING MOVEMENT-EMOTION CONNECTION

The mind-body connection allows the body and mind to have a bidirectional relationship. This allows physical movement to influence emotional states and emotional or mental states to influence the body.

For example, if you've ever been anxious while completing a task, consider how it affected your movement. Maybe you walked a little faster, became slightly clumsy, or spoke in a more jittery tone. Or maybe there was a time when you felt calm and rested. You might have moved more gracefully, had a lower tone of voice, and completed tasks at a more even pace.

The exciting thing about this bidirectional relationship is that you can use it to influence your physical and mental state. For example, when feeling anxious or jittery, you can use movement to release energy and stabilize the nervous system. In the same way, if you're feeling tense, you can work to relax the mind to relieve some of the tension.

Somatic exercises do both simultaneously.

A common problem that causes trapped emotion in people with trauma is a lack of safety within the body. Both physical and emotional trauma can result in this feeling. Pain can push us to detach from our bodies and emotions. Emotional trauma, depression, and anxiety can do the same. The more often we feel uncomfortable in our bodies and minds, the more likely we associate inner experience with unsafety. This is a big problem because we can't escape ourselves. But somatic exercises help us to feel safe within ourselves by creating small windows of safety every day.

Each time you practice a somatic exercise, the body releases endorphins, creating feelings of well-being and safety. The release of tension can feel relieving emotionally, and having a space to safely explore the discomfort of emotions is empowering. The more frequently we experience these positive feelings, the more wired our brains become for well-being.[2]

Over time, the moments of safety and well-being become longer and more of a natural state. This is because somatic movements influence our "feel-good" hormones and neurology. However, it's important to understand how to cope with uncomfortable emotions during a somatic exercise so you can safely recognize and release them.

RECOGNIZING AND RELEASING EMOTIONS

When resistance keeps you stuck, you can choose to release it to set yourself free. Emotions that surface during somatic practice are ready to be released. They might be uncomfortable, but they are only emotions. Recognizing when an emotion is trying to be released will help you see it for what it is, let go of resistance, and let the emotion move through you.

How To Recognize A Surfacing Emotion

Emotions manifest themselves in many physical symptoms and sensations. Recognizing when an emotion is surfacing will help you identify it so you can release it effectively. Somatic exercises are safe and gentle, so certain unexpected physical changes may often be trapped emotions coming to light. They may be subtle shifts, or they may be obvious. These symptoms and sensations can include:

- Physical sensations such as warmth, tingling, tightness, or tension.

- Breathing changes, such as breathing that becomes shallow, rapid, slower, or deeper.

- Facial expressions that reflect emotional states, such as smiling, frowning, or grimacing.

- Changes in heart rate, such as a racing heart or skipping a beat.

- Body movements such as trembling, shaking, or other spontaneous movements.

- Gut sensations such as butterflies, a knot in the stomach, nausea, or tightness.

- Mental shifts such as memories, flashbacks, or mood changes.

- Cathartic emotional releases such as laughing or crying.

- Vocalizations such as deep audible sighs, groaning, or other spontaneous vocalizations.

It's important to know that emotions may come up differently for everyone. You might experience a range of sensations, no additional sensations, or different sensations for different exercises. Getting to know how emotional release feels for you can help you understand when it's happening during an exercise. When you notice an emotion coming up, it's important to acknowledge it and release it if you're ready.

How To Release Emotions Safely

Releasing emotions can feel intense or scary if you're unsure what to expect or how to release them fully. If you suspect your body is trying to release trapped emotion during a somatic exercise, you can try the MY MOVE technique. It stands for:

- **M**indfulness: Practice being mindful of the emotion, acknowledging it fully.

- **Y**ield: Let the emotion exist in that moment. Don't resist it, yield to it.

- **M**ove: Use your body to move, shake, rock, wiggle, dance, or deep breathing to release.

- **O**pen: Keep your body language open to communicate safety and openness.

- **V**oice: Don't be afraid to make noises, cry, or laugh if it feels releasing.

- **E**ngage: Once the emotion has subsided, engage with your thoughts.

It's okay not to fully understand where the emotion is coming from. Take the time to immerse yourself in the experience without judgment and let the emotion flow through you. You can also take steps to set yourself up for success and feelings of safety by:

- Choosing a safe and quiet place to practice.

- Letting someone close to you know you're about to do a somatic practice.

- Using a journal to keep track of your progress and experiences.

- Reaching out for professional support to help you work through any difficult memories that have surfaced.

- Practicing your exercises with a liscenced somatic therapist if needed.

You can absolutely reap amazing results practicing somatics on your own if you are willing and able to release and work through the experiences. Somatic practice will help you build emotional resilience to better face difficult emotions in the present.

BUILDING EMOTIONAL RESILIENCE

The body-focused approach of somatic exercises strengthens your mind-body awareness so you can better recognize and release emotions. This can significantly build your emotional resilience.

Practicing these exercises regularly can decrease the tension in your body caused by long-term stress and trauma. But they also help to prevent the build-up of future tension as you learn to manage, regulate, and release emotions and stress as they arise.

The goal of somatic practice is to build a strong foundation of emotional resilience.

Emotional resilience is achieved through experience as you actively face and work through difficult emotions. This concept is a big part of somatic exercises. Emotions may take a while to come up and release once you start your practice, or you may start working through them immediately. Everyone has a unique relationship with their emotions. Somatics is about understanding how emotions come up for you and how you can release them best.

However, emotional resilience takes time and a consistent devotion to managing and regulating your emotions as best as possible. A somatic practice, even just 10 minutes per day, is enough to set you up for stability and safety from within so that you can confidently show up as your best and let stress move right through you.

A regulated nervous system balances both the body and mind. Emotions span between the two. When your emotions are allowed to flow safely through you, they no longer find places in your body to manifest for the long term. But it can be difficult to fully perceive your emotions and bodily sensations. What they mean or what they need to be released is also not always obvious

That's why cultivating a deep body awareness is vital to reap all the benefits of somatic exercises. When you're ready, make your way to the next chapter, where you will start tuning into your body and learning how to integrate your awareness into everyday life.

CULTIVATING DEEP BODY AWARENESS

Tuning Into Your Body's Language

"Attention to the human body brings healing and regeneration. Through awareness of the body we remember who we really are."

– Jack Kornfield

I had always been the calmest person in the room during a traumatic event. I could hold it together, take care of others, and do what needed to be done. In the moment, I would feel surprised by my amazing ability to cope with such hardships. And then I would crumble.

Turns out, while I was great at suppressing my emotions to get through a stressful situation, I had no idea how to manage those emotions when they eventually surfaced. They would bottle up inside of me until they'd overflow. Within hours, days, or longer, I'd unexpectedly explode with exhaustion, shock, and raw unprocessed emotion. It was either that or a deep, gnawing numbness. I struggled to escape the pattern because my emotions felt so foreign.

Everything changed when I allowed myself to slow down and *feel*.

Rather than bottling up the emotion just to get through the day, I started to make room for it. Rather than pushing through my chronic shoulder pain, I would allow myself regular breaks to acknowledge the pain and ease it. I started to prioritize well-being over being hyperproductive. My "on-the-go" nature was a symptom of survival mode.

Trauma has a way of overwhelming us. Although our instinct is often to pull back from the emotions and pain that arise, sometimes we have to lean in. Sometimes, it's better to listen a little closer so that we may understand our pain better. Becoming familiar with our pain and refusing to escape it is often the catalyst for its release.

Like a hand that grips tightly onto a balloon, our bodies hold onto trauma. By becoming attuned to our body's language and learning to speak it, we can give it permission to let go.

Being grounded in our bodies is incredibly empowering. Rather than allowing the mind to detach, weakening the mind-body connection, we can reconnect, touch base, and become fully present within ourselves using somatics. That's what this chapter is all about. I'd like to guide you through the process of enhancing your mind-body awareness so you can tune in to the unique signs of stress and relaxation your body presents, as well as how to integrate that awareness.

ENHANCING SENSORY PERCEPTION

Your sensory perception is like a muscle. When you withdraw from your emotions, ignore bodily sensations, and lose touch with yourself, your sensory perception weakens.

You might feel a well of anger pulse through your body and struggle to identify what you're feeling. You might rub arnica on your neck every night, wondering why it's always tight without understanding the core emotional cause. All your body's sensory signals feel blended. You hear the voice but can't make out the words.

Enhancing your sensory perception will allow you to tune into your body's signals to better identify your emotions and physical sensations. When you can hear what's being said, you can regulate and remedy the problems quicker and more efficiently. Well-processed pain and emotions don't need to stick around. They can deliver their message and move on.

To heighten awareness of bodily sensations, you can practice:

- Mindful breathing: Deep breathing exercises where you focus on the sensations of each inhale and exhale.

- Sensory awareness: Closing your eyes and touching different textures, taking your time to fully taste something, identifying different smells, or tuning into the sounds in your environment.

- Synchronized breath: Allowing your breath to synchronize to any physical activity such as yoga, jogging, walking, or dancing.

- Embodied mindfulness: Pulling your awareness fully into the present during everyday activities like doing the dishes, walking, or eating.

- Body scan exercise: A foundational sensory awareness exercise in somatic practice where you scan your awareness through each area of your body, noticing any sensations, tension, or relaxation you feel.

Like a muscle, practicing sensory awareness exercises will strengthen your ability to tune in and feel your bodily sensations. But it will also allow you to better understand them.

The more you feel and understand your sensations, the more patterns you will start to recognize, helping you make connections between sensations and emotional experiences. You'll start to differentiate between what sensations are there momentarily and which ones are physical cues with greater meaning.

STRESS AND RELAXATION RECOGNITION

Most involuntary bodily sensations hang in the balance between communicating stress or relaxation. Learning to understand your body's unique cues for either will allow you to feel in tune with yourself and navigate each state best.

When you can recognize your stress state kicking in early, you can take action to work through those thoughts and emotions before they progress to overwhelm. And when you can recognize signs of relaxation in your body and mind, you can identify what triggered the relaxation and take note of what's working. To help you identify patterns of relaxation or stress, here are some physical cues to look out for.

Physical Cues Of Stress

Beyond the mental impact of stress, some physical cues to indicate a stressed body or mind include:

- Muscle tension

- Headaches

- Fidgeting or nail-biting

- Fatigue

- Digestive problems

- Chest tightness

- Random aches and pains

- Rapid, shallow, or irregular breathing

- Unexplained increase or decrease in appetite

- Frowning or worried facial expression

- Increased heart rate or palpitations

- Struggling to fall or stay asleep

- Heat changes and unexplained sweating

- Dizziness or lightheadedness

- Poor immune function

- Closed off body posture

- Skin problems

- Grinding or clenching teeth

Of course, when identifying symptoms of stress, it's important to rule out other medical causes. However, when strange unexplained symptoms arise or reoccur unexpectedly, it's likely related to stress. Always see a doctor if you are concerned about a new symptom or experience worsening symptoms you suspect are related to stress.

Physical Cues Of Relaxation

Identifying states of relaxation can make them feel more rewarding and real as you consciously recognize the positive sensations. Some cues to look out for include:

- Soft, relaxed muscles

- Slow, deep and steady breathing

- Regular or slow heartbeat

- Improved digestion

- Normal, healthy appetite

- Falling asleep easily

- Feeling refreshed after sleep

- A sense of warmth and comfort

- Smiling or laughing easily

- Calm or happy facial expression

- Open, comfortable body posture

- Healthy immune function

- Improved chronic pain symptoms

Your perception of relaxation will be unique. For example, while one person may feel their body lighten during relaxation, others may feel their body growing heavier. The change will most likely be an improvement to how you felt before.

Everyone will experience a unique set of symptoms and sensations that indicate stress or relaxation. That's why it's important to determine what cues are normal for you. One of the most foundational practices in somatics is body scan practices as you have briefly experienced in Chapter 2.

BODY SCAN PRACTICES

The body scan practice is the foundation of all other somatic exercises. It is a step you should naturally include in each exercise you do from here on out. There is a full explanation and instructions for body scan practices in the next chapter. However, as the foundation of somatics, it requires some extra understanding.

During this exercise, you will close your eyes and mentally "scan" every area of your body, starting either at your toes or the top of your head. As you slowly scan your awareness through each area you will acknowledge any sensations without judgment and simultaneously breathe deeply and slowly. This process naturally indicates to your nervous system that you are safe, and it can enter the parasympathetic nervous system state, or the "rest and digest" state.

Body scan practices have long-term benefits on the nervous system as they strengthen your mind-body awareness significantly. They tune you into your nervous system and allow you to communicate with it. This is when pairing them with other exercises reaps incredible results. Providing you with that communication pathway, you can then use movement to further shift and release tension and trauma.

RESPONSIVE MOVEMENT

When you are fully tuned into your body during somatic practice it's easier to supplement or shift movements for the most benefit and release. This is called responsive movement. Because everyone is unique, responsive movement frees you up to adjust and move as necessary.

One form of responsive movement would involve accommodating your body's limits to help keep the exercises doable and comfortable. You could do any number of the adjustments mentioned in Chapter 2. However, responsive movement can also mean deepening the exercise in a way that feels releasing. For example adjusting the movement to target a certain area.

Tailoring somatic exercises to work better for you or adjusting them in the spur of the moment to accommodate new and shifting needs will deepen your practice significantly. While you will certainly feel a major difference with the exercises as they are, being flexible to change is what somatics are all about.

INTEGRATING AWARENESS INTO DAILY LIFE

Part of embracing the nervous system changes that come with somatic practice is allowing them to integrate into your everyday life. While a simple 10-minute per-day focused somatic practice is highly effective, you can deepen its impact by regularly tuning into your body throughout the day regardless of your emotional state. You can do things like:

- Pausing to take a few deep breaths

- Slowing down to savor a coffee or meal

- Grounding yourself during a conversation

- Replacing fidgeting with a short break

- Playing a song you love and dancing

- Smiling at yourself in the mirror

- Consciously easing your facial tension

- Taking stretch breaks throughout the day

- Focusing on sensations during menial tasks

Something as simple as tuning into the sensations of mundane tasks can have long-lasting positive effects on the nervous system. Tune into the coolness of the water when you wash your hands on a hot day or the roughness of a fresh towel off the line. Allow yourself the release of dancing freely around your living room to your favorite songs. Pay attention to the little signals of stress your body reveals throughout the day and remedy them with short breaks to breathe, stretch, or close your eyes. The little things add up the most.

Somatic practice is all about getting to know yourself. It's dedicating just 10 minutes a day to reconnect with your body and forge a deeper mind-body connection. It's listening to your body when you're stressed and leaning into relaxation. Learning to speak your body's language can change your life. To start planning your daily 10-minute somatic practice, turn the page to Chapter 5, where we will go through 35 truly life-changing somatic exercises. They're all simple, and anyone can do them. See you there!

35 LIFE-CHANGING SOMATIC EXERCISES

Your Comprehensive Guide To Practices Proven To Work

"When your body surrenders to movement, your soul remembers its dance."

– Gabrielle Roth

I hope you're as excited to learn these exercises as I am to share them with you. These 35 exercises are split into 6 groups, each with their own style and purpose. Some exercises are more geared towards stilling the mind and body, while others are there to shake you around and energize you. However, what they all have in common is their power and effectiveness. The sections include:

- Section 1: Revitalizing Through Breath

- Section 2: Stress And Tension Release

- Section 3: Spinal And Postural Health

- Section 4: Mindfulness And Grounding

- Section 5: Graceful Movements For Flexibility

- Section 6: Balance And Focus

As you read through the exercises, take note of which ones draw you in the most. That will be important in the final chapter of this book, where you will create your own 10-minute somatic exercise plan. When you're ready, dive into the exercises, and don't be afraid to try some of them out as you go. There will be space in your Workbook dedicated to journaling your experiences.

SECTION 1

REVITALIZING THROUGH BREATH

EXERCISE 1: DIAPHRAGMATIC BREATHING

Diaphragmatic breathing is best known as deep belly breathing, an exercise that uses the breath to activate the parasympathetic nervous system. There is a vital nerve in the parasympathetic nervous system called the vagus nerve. The diaphragm, a large balloon-like organ that sits just below the ribs, is in close contact with this nerve, allowing deep diaphragmatic breathing to stimulate it and promote relaxation. This is a great exercise to start any somatic practice with.

Instructions

This exercise can be practiced sitting up, lying down, or standing. You can intentionally find a safe space to practice it, or you can simply practice while you're on the go, such as in the car, at your work desk, or anywhere you feel comfortable doing it.

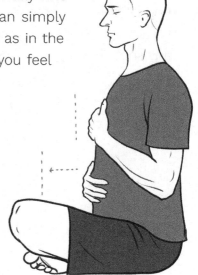

Step 1: Place One Hand On Your Chest And The Other On Your Stomach

In your chosen position, rest one hand on your stomach and the other on your chest to feel the rise and fall of each deep breath.

Step 2: Inhale Deeply And Slowly Through Your Nose

Slowly inhale through your nose, allowing the air to reach deep into your stomach. The aim is to see the hand on your stomach rise more than the one on your chest. This is how you know the air is pushing down on your diaphragm.

Step 3: Exhale Slowly Through Your Mouth

You can hold your breath in for a second or two before exhaling slowly through your mouth. Inhaling through your nose and exhaling through your mouth creates a nice rhythmic flow.

Step 4: Focus On The Rise And Fall Of Your Hands

Allow your attention to focus on the rise and fall of your hands, feeling the sensations of each breath both internally and externally.

Step 5: Repeat In A Slow Rhythmic Flow

Repeat this diaphragmatic breathing pattern for at least 5-10 breaths, making sure to keep a slow and rhythmic pace. Notice any shifts in your body and mind.

EXERCISE 2: SOMATIC SIGHING

Sighs have physiological, neurobiological, and psychological benefits.[3] They are essential for regulating our bodies and minds. Intentional somatic sighing is a way to use the function of a sigh to help us experience the benefits of sighing on purpose. A somatic sigh is an audible sigh used to release emotion or tension. It activates the parasympathetic nervous system, promoting relaxation.

Instructions

The somatic sigh is best practiced standing or sitting down with your spine straight and your shoulders square. Find a place where you can feel comfortable making audible sighs without holding back.

Step 1: Inhale Deeply Through Your Nose

Take a long, deep inhale through your nose as you would during a diaphragmatic breathing exercise. Feel the breath fill your stomach.

Step 2: Release The Breath In An Audible Sigh

Allow the breath to flood out of your mouth in an audible sighing sound. Release the full exhale as you notice any tension melt away.

Step 4: Become Mindful Of The Sensations That Arise

After each sigh, notice any changes or sensations you experience. Let those sensations help govern the continuation of the exercise.

Step 3: Repeat As Needed

You can repeat the audible sigh as many times as you like or until you experience a sense of relaxation. 1-5 somatic sighs are generally enough to experience a shift. You can also take a couple of normal breaths in between each somatic sigh.

EXERCISE 3: SOMATIC BREATH COUNTING

Focusing our attention on our breathing is naturally a great way to distract ourselves from pain or anxiety, but also to center the mind and improve mental clarity. To enhance the therapeutic impact of focusing on the breath, we can combine it with counting in a rhythmic fashion. Somatic breath counting is an excellent grounding practice for stilling busy thoughts and promoting a sense of calm. It is a mindfulness breathing practice.

Instructions

Somatic breath counting can be practiced in any position. You can complete the exercise anywhere at any time, even with others around. It also serves as an excellent regulation strategy for heightened emotions.

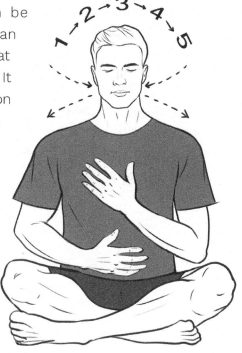

Step 1: Focus Your Attention On Your Normal Breathing

Bring your awareness to your breath, allowing yourself to breathe as normal for a moment. Pay attention to the natural rhythmic flow of your breath.

Step 2: Start Counting Each Inhale And Exhale

As you begin counting, start with 1 on your inhale and 2 on your exhale. Continue until you reach number 5. So inhale, 1, exhale, 2, inhale, 3, exhale, 4, inhale 5.

Step 3: Create A Continuous Loop

Because you ended at 5 on an inhale, your next exhale will be 1, creating a continuous loop. Simply continue to count from 1-5 regardless of which numbers fall on an inhale or exhale.

Step 4: Maintain Your Awareness

You may feel your mind start to lose focus from time to time. If this happens, gently refocus your awareness onto your breath, synchronizing your counting from 1 again.

Step 5: Experiment With The Length Of The Exercise

Although this exercise can work rapidly, you can reap more benefits by practicing it for longer. Set a timer for 1-5 minutes and experiment with how long you can maintain your focus. Challenge yourself! This exercise can promote better focus and mental clarity long after it's over.

EXERCISE 4: HUMMING

Humming is one of the most highly effective, commonly used, and ancient somatic practices. As the first somatic exercise I ever consciously tried, I'm excited to tell you why. Just as diaphragmatic breathing can directly stimulate the vagus nerve, so can humming. Humming reverberates through the vocal chords which are close to the most exposed area of the vagus nerve, the parts that run along either side of our neck. This stimulation triggers the activation of our parasympathetic nervous system, enabling relaxation.

Instructions

Find a comfortable place to sit, stand, or lie down. It's advisable to have some privacy or be with people you feel safe and comfortable around. While you can hum gently, it's truly great to be able to fully release during this exercise.

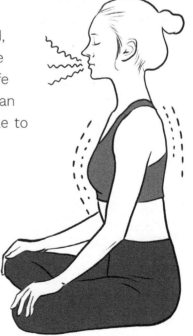

Step 1: Inhale Deeply Through Your Nose

Take a deep diaphragmatic breath in through your nose, feeling your belly expand, and get ready to release it in a hum.

Step 2: Release The Breath In A Hum

On the exhale, keep your lips closed and make a humming sound. Let the vibrations reverberate through your head, throat, and chest.

Step 3: Tune Into The Sensations

As the vibrations spread through your body, focus on where you feel them most, how they feel, and notice any relaxation cues you experience.

Step 4: Experiment With The Pitch

Play around with the pitch of your humming. Try a deep hum and see how far down your chest you can feel the vibrations. Try a higher-pitched hum and notice the areas of your face in which you experience the most vibration. Find pitches that you feel bring on the most relaxation.

Step 5: Bring Your Awareness To How You Feel

After a few breaths of humming, tune into your body and mind. Notice how you feel and pay attention to any shifts you experience.

SECTION 2

STRESS AND
TENSION RELEASE

EXERCISE 5: PROGRESSIVE MUSCLE RELAXATION

Also known as PMR, progressive muscle relaxation is designed to create awareness of any physical muscle tension you may be holding onto as well as offer a way to release it. Tensing muscles to release tension may seem contradictory, but systematically contracting and relaxing muscles can help release chronic muscle tension, build an awareness of muscle groups, manage stress, and promote relaxation.

Instructions

This exercise is best practiced lying down or sitting in a comfortable position. Choose somewhere quiet and private to practice this exercise. It's also advised to start this exercise by centering yourself with a few deep breaths.

Step 1: Start At Your Feet

Once you are centered and comfortable, bring your awareness to your feet and contract the muscles as much as you can comfortably squeeze. Feel your toes curl and your arch pull inward.

Step 2: Hold For 5-10 Seconds

Hold the tension in your feet for up to about 10 seconds and get ready to release.

Step 3: Release The Tension Fully

Suddenly release the tension completely and bring your awareness to the sensations of relaxation moving through the muscles.

Step 4: Repeat On Each Muscle Group

From your feet, progressively move up your body, tensing and releasing one muscle group at a time. Tense and release your lower legs, then your upper legs. Move up towards your buttocks, pelvis, and hips, then your abs and lower back. Tense and release your chest, then your arms and hands, then your neck, and end with your face.

Step 5: Focus On The Contrast

As you move up your body, and after you're all done, take a moment to notice the contrast between tension and relaxation across all muscle groups. Notice any shifts within your body both mentally and physically.

EXERCISE 6: BODY SCAN MEDITATION

As we've briefly covered before, the body scan somatic exercise, also known as the body scan meditation, is one of the foundational somatic practices for increasing mind-body awareness and tension release. As you scan your awareness throughout your body, your perception of those areas naturally heightens, revealing insights into your sensory and psychological experience. A strong mind-body connection empowers you to tune into your body for information that can lead to better releases and relaxation.

Instructions

You can complete this exercise in any position you'd like, but lying down with legs straight and arms at either side may be the most impactful. This position leaves less room for your environment to interfere with your sensory perception.

Step 1: Focus On Your Breathing

Start this exercise by bringing your awareness to your breathing and slowing your breath to a nice, even rhythm for a relaxing start.

Step 2: Start Your Scan At Your Toes

Bring your awareness to your toes and focus there for a second, taking note of any sensations or tension in the area.

Step 3: Scan Your Body Systematically

From your toes, move your awareness up your legs and through your body, taking a moment to mentally "scan" and perceive each area. Notice any sensations or tension along the way. Sensations you can bring your awareness to include warmth, coolness, softness, or tension.

Step 4: Release The Tension You Find

If you find areas of tension, focus your awareness on them for a moment and invite the tension to ease up. Consciously soften the muscle and imagine it melting into the floor.

Step 5: Move On Without Judgement And Recenter

Remember to stay mindful throughout this practice. Don't judge a sensation or resist it. Simply bring your awareness to it and be prepared to release it. When you've scanned your entire body, recenter your awareness.

EXERCISE 7: PALM PUSHING

Palm pushing is a somatic exercise that you can use to target tension release in the upper body. The exercise allows you to release specified tension by tensing and releasing the full set of upper body muscles. It's an exercise that can help with chronic tension in areas such as the shoulders, arms, upper back, and hands.

Instructions

This exercise is best practiced sitting up straight. Find a comfortable seated position in a quiet, private area. Take a few deep breaths before starting, and be sure to keep a regular breathing pattern throughout.

Step 1: Bring Your Hands Together With Palms Touching

Lift your hands with palms touching in a prayer position. Hold them together lightly in front of your chest.

Step 2: Push Your Palms Together With A Gentle Pressure

Now apply pressure between your palms, pushing them together with a gentle but firm force. Allow all your upper body muscles to engage and tense.

Step 3: Hold For A Few Seconds

Maintain the pressure between your palms for a few seconds. Keep the pressure comfortable and even make sure not to strain.

Step 4: Gradually Release The Tension

Keeping your palms together, slowly and gradually release the pressure and feel the tension release from each muscle in your upper body.

Step 5: Repeat As Needed

Continue to reapply and release the pressure between your palms as needed, paying attention to the contrast between the two states.

EXERCISE 8: LEG SHAKING

Neurogenic tremors are our body's natural regulating response to stress and trauma. We can see it in full action amongst wild animals, where an animal nearly escapes harm, and within seconds of being in safety, it shakes its body. Humans have this same mechanism that we have been conditioned to suppress to maintain appearances. However, this regulatory response is vital to releasing tension and trauma. Thankfully, we can simulate it for the same benefits with this leg-shaking somatic exercise.

Instructions

Find a comfortable place to sit or lie down where you won't be disturbed. Along with the incredible physical release you may experience, be prepared for any potential emotions to come up as well.

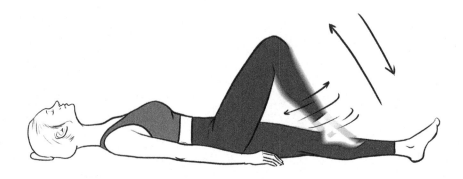

Step 1: Start With One Leg At A Time

If you're lying down, keep your knees slightly bent as you begin. Start with one leg, lifting it a couple of centimeters off the ground and shaking it vigorously. Allow the shaking to fully extend up your leg, freely and loosely.

Step 2: Tune Into The Sensations As You Shake

Continue to shake your leg for about 20-30 seconds, tuning into the sensations and vibrations you feel. Allow the shaking to loosen up any tension you may have. If you feel an emotion come up, use the intensity of the shaking to release it.

Step 3: Switch Legs And Repeat

Fully relax your legs again and switch. Lift the next leg and repeat steps 1 and 2, vigorously shaking and tuning into the sensations. After 20-30 seconds, relax both legs again.

Step 4: Try Shaking Both Legs For An Optional Full Body Experience

If you're comfortable giving it a try, progress the exercise to achieve a full body shaking by lifting and shaking both legs simultaneously. Allow the shaking to vibrate up the entire body and release stored tension and trauma throughout. Continue for 20-30 seconds.

Step 5: Reconnect With Stillness

After the shaking, sit or lie in stillness for a moment. Bring your awareness to the sensations you feel after shaking. Notice the contrast between the intensity of shaking and the sudden stillness. Take a deep breath in and exhale.

EXERCISE 9: TRAUMA-RELEASING EXERCISES (TRE)

These exercises, known as Trauma-Releasing Exercises, or TRE, are a set of lower body movements designed to fatigue muscles in a way that naturally induces the body's shaking or tremoring mechanism. There are 7 short exercises developed by Dr. David Berceli, which you complete in sequence to unlock stored trauma and tension.

Instructions

We're going to work with 4 of the standing TRE exercises plus the final floor sequence. Keep your breathing deep and flowing throughout. Once your body begins to tremor, let it flow for as long as you'd like. You can stop the tremoring at any time by simply changing your position.

Exercise 1: Heel Lift Calf Raises

Standing with your weight balanced on your right foot, using your left foot for gentle balance, complete about a minute of calf raises or until your muscle fatigue is at a 7/10. Repeat on the left leg.

Exercise 2: Hip Sits For Hips And Thighs

Stand with your weight balanced on your right foot, using your left leg to stay stable. Then continuously bend your right knee in a sitting motion until a 7/10 fatigue. Repeat on the left leg.

Exercise 3: Foreward Fold Stretch

Stand with your feet past hip-width apart. Fold forward and let your fingers hang to the floor. Gently walk your fingers from your right leg to your left, pausing at each to hold and breath.

Exercise 4: Wall Sit

Rest your back against a solid wall with your legs in a seated position. You should be able to see the tops of your feet to make the exercise feel easier. Hold this position until you reach a 7/10 muscle fatigue or start to tremor lightly. You can allow the tremor if you're comfortable.

Exercise 5: Floor Sequence

When you're ready, move onto the floor and lie flat on your back with your knees raised and feet on the ground. Slowly drop your knees into a butterfly position and rest here for a moment. Then, slowly pull your knees together, leaving a couple of inches of space between them and hold. Alternate between these two rested positions, allowing any tremors that happen to flow through you. If at any point you feel you'd like the tremors to stop, simply straighten your legs and rest.

EXERCISE 10: SOMATIC WRITING

Somatic writing is an excellent way to release emotions and stress by expressing yourself across the pages of a journal. Part of somatic release is releasing what is in your mind, especially when it's in a way that you can see and reflect on easily, such as with writing or painting. It is a great exercise for increasing emotional awareness, self-reflection, and stress release.

Instructions

Sit comfortably with a journal and a pen in a place where you won't be disturbed. Be prepared to write without a filter, even if you have to dispose of the paper afterward. If you can keep your journals private, it's a great practice to keep them for future reflection. However, many people like to burn or shred their journal pages.

Step 1: Set An Intention

Before you start writing, take a moment to acknowledge the emotions you feel or your mental state. Decide on an intention for your journaling that you feel most called to in this moment, such as releasing thoughts and emotions or gaining clarity and insights.

Step 2: Start Writing Freely

Without judgment or thought, allow the writing to flow freely onto the paper. Let your stream of consciousness be expressed without censorship. It doesn't matter if the writing is neat or makes much sense. Be detailed and descriptive when addressing how you feel.

Step 3: Bring Your Awareness To Your Body

As you write, take a mental note of any physical changes or sensations you may experience. Notice any somatic experiences such as tension, softness, warmth, trembling, or any of the cues you learned in Chapter 4. See them as a release so your stress can move on.

Step 4: Reflect And Integrate

Once you feel done and ready take a few deep breaths. Take a moment to sit with what you wrote, reading it through and reflecting on it. Allow the insights to integrate by acknowledging your emotions and thoughts. Try to validate how you feel and refrain from judgment.

Step 5: Repeat Regularly

For somatic writing to be the most effective, try to implement it in your daily routine when you usually feel the most stress, such as after a long day. However, it's a great tool for emotional regulation for those times when your thoughts and emotions feel intense and out of control.

EXERCISE 11: GUIDED IMAGERY

The mind is a powerful thing that often can't differentiate between imagined scenarios and real life. Guided imagery is a way to train your brain into the parasympathetic nervous system state simply by vividly imagining you are in a safe and relaxing environment. It is a form of guided meditation.

Instructions

Find a comfortable place to sit or lie down where you won't be disturbed. You can either choose to follow a recorded guided visualization or you can proceed to self-guide the imagery.

Step 1: Take A Few Deep Breaths

Center yourself and prepare for relaxation with a few deep diaphragmatic breaths.

Step 2: Decide On An Imagined Location To Visit

Think about a place you would like to relax in, such as a beachfront, a forest, a fantasy location, or wherever you'd like. This could also be a relaxing scenario like receiving a massage, going on a train ride, or whatever scenario you feel is relaxing.

Step 3: Close Your Eyes And Begin Visualizing

With your eyes closed, walk yourself through the visualization. Imagine all the various details of the location or situation.

Step 4: Engage Your Senses

Let your senses come to life within the visualization. Visualize the smells, the colors and objects you can see, the things you can touch, and the noises you can hear. For example, you can feel the cool water of a forest stream, listen to the seagulls at the beach, or feel the warmth of hot massage stones being placed on your back. Try to be as present as possible in your visualization.

Step 5: Complete The Exercise With A Body Scan

While in this fictional location, complete a body scan, bringing your awareness from your toes to your head. Notice any changes you feel and acknowledge them. Before you open your eyes, feel the visualization drifting away as you slowly move your physical body again. Finish with a few deep breaths and notice any relaxation cues you feel.

SECTION 3

SPINAL AND
POSTURAL HEALTH

EXERCISE 12: PELVIC TILTS

A fantastic somatic practice for relieving lower back pain and tension is the pelvic tilt. The rocking motion of the pelvis helps to loosen up the muscles in the lower back and pelvis, releasing stored tension and promoting flexibility. Practicing regular pelvic tilts can contribute to improved lower back health.

Instructions

Find a comfortable place to lie flat on your back. Relax your upper body and neck fully with your knees bent and feet flat on the ground. Your feet should be hip-width apart.

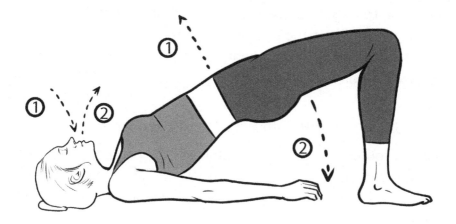

Step 1: Start By Engaging Your Core Muscles

Your core muscles will provide you with the stability to complete this exercise. Simply engage them enough to assist you without the tension influencing your steady breathing.

Step 2: Tilt Your Pelvis Forward

With steady control, tilt your pelvis forward so your tailbone moves further beneath you. This should create a deeper arch in your lower back.

Step 3: Release The Pelvic Tilt And Deepen

Relax your pelvis, allowing your lower back to return to a neutral position. Now deepen this pelvic release by pushing your lower back into the ground so your tailbone lifts further up

Step 4: Create A Rocking Motion By Repeating Steps 2 & 3

Continue to tilt your pelvis back and forth in a gentle, controlled rocking motion. Let the floor massage the muscles in this area, and the controlled movements tighten and loosen them to release tension.

Step 5: Sync Your Breath With The Movement

Take a moment to sync your breathing to the pelvic tilt. Inhale on the forward tilt, and exhale as you release and deepen. Repeat for a minute or 2, noticing any sensations or shifts in tension around the area.

EXERCISE 13: SPINAL TWISTS

Spinal twists are a gentle yet highly effective tension release exercise for increasing flexibility, releasing tension, and reducing stiffness along the entire spine. This exercise can contribute to overall spinal health, an increased range of motion, and more sustained feelings of well-being. You can use it for basic tension release or to help release spinal discomfort.

Instructions

You can do this exercise in a lying down or seated position with one simple alteration. Find a comfortable place with enough space to extend your legs out or twist your arms around. Prepare to use your breath to deepen this spinal twist.

Step 1:

Lengthen Your Spine On The Inhale

Whether seated or lying down, take a deep breath in as you feel your spine lengthening. Imagine creating spaces between each vertebrae.

Step 2: Start With A Light Spinal Twist On The Exhale

If seated, place your right hand on your left knee and twist your spine as you exhale, looking over your left shoulder. If you're lying down flat on your back, bring your right knee up and allow it to slowly drop across to the left as your shoulders stay flat on the floor.

Step 3: Feel The Rotation Of Your Spine

Allow your hand to pull you deeper into the stretch, but try not to strain. The stretch should feel releasing and comfortable.

Step 4: Hold For A Few Breaths

Hold the spinal twist as you continue to breathe. Breathe in deeply and use each exhale to release tension or deepen the twist.

Step 5: Repeat On The Other Side

Take a deep breath in and allow the exhale to soften the spinal twist. Bring your position back to the center slowly and repeat on the other side. Continue to alternate sides and tune into the tension you feel. If you feel a tight spot, take a deep breath in and use the exhale plus your hand to work through the tension.

EXERCISE 14: CAT-COW STRETCH

This fun somatic exercise, known as the cat-cow stretch, is popular in everyday yoga practices. It uses the alternating of two poses to balance spinal muscles and release tension along the upper back and neck in particular. This stretch increases blood flow to these areas, increasing flexibility and mobility along your entire spine.

Instructions

You can do this exercise on the floor or your bed. You will need to get on all fours with knees hip-width apart. Hold your neck in a neutral posture, facing down, and avoid hunching your shoulders.

Step 1: Inhale Deeply And Move Into Cow Pose

When you're ready, take a nice deep inhale through your nose as you arch your back and lift your head. You can also push your shoulder blades down, lift your gaze, and tilt your pelvis back.

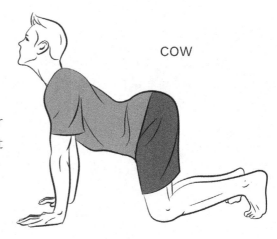

COW

Step 3: Hold

Hold the position for a full, long inhale and a short push at the end, feeling the muscles throughout your back almost squeezing.

Step 2: Move Into Cat Pose As You Exhale

CAT

As you release the exhale, move your body into the opposite position, rounding your back like a cat and dropping your chin, shoulders, and pelvis in.

Step 3: Create A Flow Between The Poses

Continue to inhale and exhale now, creating a flow between the cat and cow poses. Allow the breath to deepen the stretch and circulate throughout your body.

Step 5: Explore Variations

As you become more comfortable with this exercise and have built up more spinal flexibility and mobility, you can explore some variations for a deeper tension release. Rather than just moving the pose up and down, you can circle your neck and hips to add more fluidity. This will further improve your flexibility and mobility, but only try it if it feels flowing and comfortable.

EXERCISE 15: ROLLING DOWN THE SPINE

The rolling down the spine somatic exercise is a gentle spinal release aimed at releasing tension along the spine while improving flexibility. It's an easy standing exercise that can be used as a simple warm-up stretch or full somatic exercise. It's a great opportunity to close your eyes and really sink into your body from a standing position.

Instructions

Find a private place where you can safely stand with enough room in front of you to bend forward and down. I recommend closing your eyes and using this exercise to soften your body.

Step 1: Straighten And Lengthen Your Posture

As you inhale deeply through your nose, straighten your posture and imagine a string pulling your spine up towards the ceiling from the top of your head.

Step 2: Exhale And Roll Your Body Down

On the exhale, start by dropping your chin, softening your shoulders inward, and rolling your body down until your upper body is completely folded over. You can bend your knees slightly to keep this exercise soft and relaxing.

Step 3: Remain Standing And Relax Forward

As you hold your body up with your legs, allow your upper body to completely relax forward. Let your upper body hang softly toward the ground, feeling all the tension in your spine melt away. Take a couple of deep breaths in.

Step 4: Inhale And Roll Your Body Back Up Again

On the next big inhale, slowly roll your body back up again, starting at the hips, moving along the spine, and ending with your shoulders and chin. Repeat step 1 again.

Step 5: Repeat As Needed

Continue to roll your body down, resting in a forward fold for a moment, and rolling back up again as long as needed. Enjoy the sensations and softening you feel.

EXERCISE 16: CHILD'S POSE

The child's pose yoga position is a somatic exercise intended to fully release and relax the entire body. It is a resting position perfect for ending a somatic practice or completing before bed. This exercise promotes feelings of comfort within the body and mind, preparing the body for rest and release.

Instructions

Find a comfortable place on the floor or bed where you can kneel quietly. This is a kneeling, forward bend position that will release tension throughout your entire body, but mostly along your spine. Keep your breath flowing throughout and your eyes closed.

Step 1: Bring Feet Together And Knees Apart

As you kneel on the floor or bed, soften your feet beneath yourself and open the knees enough to make space for your body to fit between. Sit back on your heels comfortably.

Step 2: Fold Your Torso Over With Arms Stretched Forward

Bring your torso down between your knees with your arms stretched out in front of you. Allow your palms to pull your torso forward as you fully relax your upper body.

Step 3: Breathe Deeply And Relax

Spend as long as you need to in this pose, completely relaxing your entire body. You can sink your hips back or reposition yourself in any way that feels good.

Step 4: Explore Variations

Some variations of child's pose include resting your forehead on the ground in front of your knees to stretch out your neck muscles, bend your arms to rest your head on the backs of your hands instead, or bringing your arms back completely, allowing your shoulders and arms to soften fully. You can also increase the support under your body with a pillow or folded blanket to enable full relaxation.

Step 5: Exit Child's Pose Gently

This exercise requires a slow and gentle exit to maintain the softness and relaxation. To exit this pose, slowly walk your hands back, allowing your arms to lift your upper body out of the position. Take your time with this, and notice any sensations you feel.

EXERCISE 17: SEATED FORWARD BEND

The seated forward bend is a yoga position also known as Paschimottanasana. Although it is a simple stretch because it stretches both the back and legs, the spinal release is increased. Tight leg muscles, particularly the hamstrings, can contribute to lower back tightness. The seated forward bend relieves tension in all the muscles associated with spinal health, from head to toe.

Instructions

Find a comfortable place on the floor or a bed where you won't be disturbed. This stretch can be quite effective, so if the full stretch is too difficult, only bend as far forward as you're comfortable with.

Step 1: Sit Up Straight With Legs Straight Forward

Sit up with your back straight and your legs long in front of you.

Step 2: Inhale And Prepare To Stretch

Prepare to stretch by allowing the soles of your feet to flex up as if you were standing. Rest your hands on your knees and inhale deeply through your nose and into your belly.

Step 3: Exhale And Bend Forward

Exhale slowly through your mouth as you bend forward. You can bend as far as is comfortable, challenging yourself enough to feel the stretch along your legs and spine.

Step 4: Hold For A Few Breaths And Repeat

Hold the stretch for a few deep breaths. You can also use the breath to deepen the stretch if you'd like. Use your hands to gently pull you into a deeper bend. When you're reading, slowly return to normal, and repeat as necessary.

Step 5: Specify Your Variation

There are two variations to this forward bend: one that is more gentle and relaxing, and one that aims to deepen the stretch along your legs. You will likely already be in variation one, bending forward with a more rounded back. However, for a much deeper leg stretch try to keep your back straighter and bend only at the hips.

EXERCISE 18: STANDING FORWARD BEND

The standing forward bend is a powerful yoga pose also known as Uttanasana. It is a deeper and more difficult forward bend in comparison to the seated forward bend. Often, what intensifies these bends is the angle of the foot. Standing deepens the stretch significantly as your foot is fully flexed with gravity aiding the upper body's bend.

Instructions

Find a quiet place with enough space to bend forward fully with your body. You don't need to be able to touch your toes for this bend, simply stretch down as much as you're comfortable with.

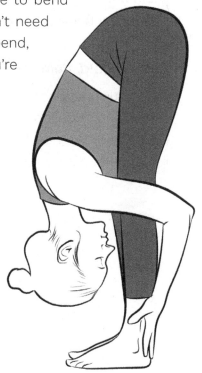

Step 1: Stand Up Straight And Inhale Deeply

Prepare for your stretch by standing up straight and taking a long, slow inhale deep into your belly.

Step 2: Hinge Forward At The Hips

On the exhale, hinge forward at the hips while keeping your back straight.

Lead with your chest and reach your hands down as you bend forward.

Step 3: Rest In the Stretch

Once you're as far forward as you can comfortably stretch, allow your hands to drop where they can rest. If you can touch the floor with your fingertips, allow them to hang there. Or, if they are above the ground, rest them on the part of your legs or feet that they're closest to.

Step 4: Deepen With The Breath

As you breathe in and out, use your exhales to deepen the stretch. Continue to hinge forward at the hips and notice the changes in your hand position. You can also use your hands to help pull you forward by holding them behind your knees.

Step 5: Hold, Release, And Repeat

Hold your final position for a couple of breaths, tuning into the sensations throughout your body and release when you're ready. Feel the difference between the stretching tension and soft release. Repeat as necessary.

SECTION 4

MINDFULNESS
AND GROUNDING

EXERCISE 19: GROUNDING EXERCISES

There are various grounding exercises with the same goal in mind: to center your awareness and ground you into the present moment. These exercises are an excellent way to reconnect with the earth and reality as a whole, fostering a sense of inner stability, safety, and relaxation. These tools are most effective at reducing stress, relieving anxiety, and stabilizing mood.

Instructions

I'm going to share 3 simple grounding exercises with you. Find a quiet place to sit, stand, or lie down where you won't be disturbed. However, many of these exercises can be practiced in the heat of a stressful moment to help ground you.

Exercise 1: The Five Senses

For this exercise you will use your senses to ground you into the present moment: Sight, sound, smell, touch, and taste. Find 5 things in your environment you can see, 4 things you can hear, 3 things you can touch, 2 things you can smell, and 1 thing you can taste. As you engage with each sense, try to fully immerse yourself in the experience as you feel your awareness centering.

For example, if you're drinking a cup of coffee, notice the painting on your wall, the radio playing, the smell of the coffee, the feel of your sofa, and the taste of the sip you take.

SMELL

TASTE

SIGHT

SOUND

TOUCH

SOMATIC EXERCISES

Exercise 2: Barefoot Walking

The simplest way to ground a human being is by reconnecting with the earth. Because we often live very detached lives from nature, with technology, shoes, and supermarkets, feeling grounded in such an unnatural world is difficult. To reconnect with nature and physically ground your body to the earth, take off your shoes and walk barefoot.

As you walk, feel the sensations beneath your feet. Try to walk on various terrains to enhance this experience. Find some grass to walk on, then stones, then pavement. Feel the difference in sensations.

ROOTING
VISUALIZATION

Exercise 3: Rooting Visualization

A rooting visualization is a great way to shift your perspective and feel grounded in the earth. As you're sitting or standing, close your eyes and visualize a root growing out the bottom of your feet and down into the earth. As the root grows down, visualize the core of the earth glowing a color of your choice. When your root reaches the core of the earth, the color spreads up your roots and through your body. Tune into any sensations you might feel.

EXERCISE 20: MINDFUL WALKING

Mindful walking is a mindfulness exercise that encourages contemplation, heightened awareness, and relaxation. It takes something most of us do every day and transforms it into a time of peaceful gratitude. Mindful walking cultivates mindfulness through intentional, focused walking which will allow you to more easily ground into the present when needed.

Instructions

Find a place where you can safely walk without obstacles. You can alternate between open and closed eyes if possible, deepening the experience.

Step 1: Start At A Standstill

Stand still and upright for a moment, taking deep breaths to help you center. Take a moment to observe your surroundings, engaging each of your senses if possible and heightening your awareness. Continue to breathe deeply throughout the exercise.

Step 2: Set An Intention

Decide on an intention for your mindful walk. It can be something like finding clarity on a topic, practicing focus, stress reduction, or simply enjoyment.

Step 3: Begin Walking Slowly

Bring your awareness to your body now and start walking slowly. Allow each step to be focused and intentional.

Step 4: Focus On Every Sensation

Allow your awareness to be fully present in each sensation. Feel the soles of your feet flexing and arching. Feel the weight of your foot as it swings forward. Feel your arms gently swaying. Tune into the experience and be as present and grounded as possible. Notice every sensation of walking that you normally don't truly experience.

Step 5: Mindfully Conclude

When you're ready to conclude the exercise, slowly bring your awareness back from your body and into your environment again. Focus on the sights, sounds, smells, and anything else you can. Allow your breath to return to normal, and take some time to reflect on the experience.

EXERCISE 21: EYE PALMING

The eyes are a common place for tension to build. But because they are also responsible for sight, eye palming works to relax us in two very effective ways. By covering the eyes with our palms, we not only help relieve tension and pressure but we cut off visual stimuli, which can help calm the mind.

Instructions

You can do this exercise sitting, standing, or lying down, provided you are in a safe place. This exercise is best used during the day to help maintain a sense of calm, but you can use it whenever needed.

Step 1: Prepare Your Hands

Rub your palms together to create some friction, the warmth will produce a more comforting experience. Cup your hands gently to create a slight hollow in closed hands.

Step 2: Cover your Eyes

Bring your palms up to your eyes, covering them as much as possible without applying too much pressure. The hollows of your palms should create a small space above each eye so you can open them. If you're struggling to cut out all the light, adjust your hands as needed.

Step 3: Take Deep Breathes

Start taking deep breaths to bring a sense of calm and relaxation.

Step 4: Hold And Feel The Sensation Of Darkness

Hold your hands in place for a few deep breaths and allow yourself to feel the sensation of darkness on your eyes. Soften the tension in your brow and allow your eyes to rest.

Step 5: Remove Slowly And Gently

When you're ready, slowly soften your hands and allow the light back in. Gently open your eyes and take note of how your eyes feel. They will likely feel refreshed and clear.

EXERCISE 22:
SOMATIC VISUALIZATION

Somatic visualization is a powerful tool promoting relaxation and tension release with nothing but the power of the mind. It involves putting imagery around our tension to help us let go and release. Practiced regularly, this somatic practice can increase body awareness, reduce stress, and improve your sense of well-being.

Instructions

Find a comfortable place to sit or lie down where you won't be disturbed. However, lying down is recommended. Close your eyes and breathe deeply throughout this exercise.

Step 1: Start With A Body Scan

As you breathe deeply and hold your eyes closed, proceed with a body scan. Pause to acknowledge any areas of tension or discomfort.

Step 2: Give Your Tension A Color And Shape

Start with one area of tension or discomfort if there are many. Give your tension or discomfort a shape, color, size, or any other visualization that makes sense to you. For example, you could see your tension as a dark mist, a tight knot of rope, a heavy cloud, or a murky puddle.

Step 3: Visually Release The Tension

Holding your awareness on this area of tension, choose a way to visually release the tension in a way that makes sense with its shape. For example, you can visualize the tight knot becoming untangled, the dark mist escaping with every exhale, and the murky puddle being washed clean by a stream of water. Whatever feels right for you, visualize the tension releasing.

Step 4: Tune Into Sensations

As you visualize the tension leaving your body, try to feel the physical release. Tune into any sensations you feel, and imagine the physical tension softening and fading as you release.

Step 5: Repeat For Each Area

If there are multiple areas of tension or discomfort, you can repeat the steps for each area. However, if you are pressed for time or there are too many areas, simply visualize each area and release simultaneously. For example, if all your tension is dark mist, visualize your breath collecting the mist on the inhale and releasing it on the exhale.

EXERCISE 23: YOGA SUN SALUTATIONS

Sun salutations are a series of yoga poses completed in what is known as a flow with the intention of energizing the body and improving the mind-body connection. There are 12 positions in total which together warm up, stretch, and strengthen the entire body.

Instructions

Find a comfortable place where you will have enough room to stretch out. You can either alternate breathing per pose, or you can pause in each position allowing the breath to flow.

Position 1: Mountain Pose

Stand tall with feet hip-width apart and bring your palms together in front of your chest.

Position 2: Upward Salute

Keeping your palms together, inhale deeply, and reach your palms up above your head.

Position 3: Forward Fold

As you exhale, fold forward at the hips, dropping your hands down onto your shins or feet.

SOMATIC EXERCISES

Position 4: Plank Position

Bend your knees, press your weight onto your palms, and step back into a plank position.

Position 5: Upward Facing Dog

Move from your toes onto the backs of your feet, then dip your hips and arch your back.

Position 6: Downward Facing Dog

Step onto your toes pressing your weight back with your palms. Drop your head and lift your hips.

Position 7: Forward Fold

Step both feet forward back to standing, with your upper body bent over in a forward fold again.

Position 8: Upward Salute

Inhale deeply, lifting your arms high above your head and placing your palms back together.

Position 9: Mountain Pose

Slowly lower your palms back in front of your chest and finish in mountain pose. Repeat 1-9.

SECTION 5

GRACEFUL MOVEMENTS FOR FLEXIBILITY

EXERCISE 24: TAI CHI MOVEMENTS

Tai Chi is an ancient form of Martial Arts, originating in China. The movements are slow, smooth, and deliberate to encourage balance and calm throughout the body and mind. This practice promotes mind-body awareness, relaxation, and overall well-being. There are many movements within the practice ranging from balancing positions, arm movements, and steady postures.

Instructions

Find a peaceful area to practice, where you can move freely without obstruction. I'm going to share an introduction to one of the most popular Tai Chi movement sequences known as Grasp the Sparrows tail.

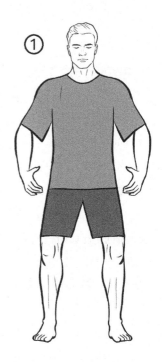

Position 1: Starting Position

Standing in a relaxed and upright position, step your feet out shoulder-width apart. Tuck your pelvis in, bend your knees slightly, and keep your spine straight. Bring your awareness to your breath, inhaling and exhaling slowly.

Position 2: Ward Off

Start with the left leg, you will come back to this step after position 5 and redo the sequence with the opposite leg and arm. Step your left leg to the side, turn your torso with it, and shift your balance onto your left leg. Expand your arms in a circular motion, leading with the left arm.

Position 3: Roll Back

Continue the circular motion of your arms, bringing both back towards your body and to the other side while simultaneously shifting your weight back to your other leg.

Position 4: Press

Now bring your hands together into the center of your chest, shifting your weight back onto your front leg and pressing the hands forward.

Position 5: Push

From the press position, round the hands back toward the stomach with palms facing outward as you shift your weight into a more centered position. Then shift your weight forward again as you push your palms forward and slightly up together.

Position 6: Pivot To The Other Side And Repeat

Shift your weight and pivot to the center, with your arms in the middle. Repeat on the other side.

106

EXERCISE 25: BUTTERFLY POSE

The butterfly yoga pose, also known as Baddha Konasana in Sanskrit, is a seated hip opening pose that increases flexibility and mobility in the hips and groin areas. Along with releasing tension in the pelvic region, it is also known to have a calming effect on the nervous system, promoting relaxation and well-being.

Instructions

This is a seated position, best practiced in a quiet and comfortable environment. If the position is too difficult, you can use yoga blocks or cushions underneath your knees to support your legs.

Step 1: Sit Up Straight With Legs Extended

Take a moment to sit up straight with your legs extended in front of you. Take a couple of deep breaths to center yourself. Keep your back straight throughout this exercise.

Step 2: Bend Your Knees And Bring Feet Together

When you're ready, bend your knees and bring the soles of your feet together. Your knees should be resting in this position in order to stretch and open the hips.

Step 3: Hold Your Feet

Hold your feet with your hands, using them to help bring your feet closer in toward yourself. This should deepen the stretch and prepare you for step 4.

Step 4: Deepen With Butterfly Wings

If you're comfortable deepening this stretch, gently rock your knees up and down, as if flapping butterfly wings.

Step 5: Release Slowly

Enjoy this tension-relieving exercise for as long as you'd like. However, when you're ready to finish, release your feet from the position slowly.

EXERCISE 26: CROSS-CRAWL EXERCISE

This fun somatic exercise, known as the cross-crawl exercise, is a coordinated movement that uses the entire body to engage the left and right hemispheres of the brain. The cross-crawl is an easy and effective way to enhance coordination and cognitive function by helping to balance and tone the nervous system.

Instructions

Find a quiet place where you can stand up straight and complete this exercise. It can be completed on the ground if you have sliding pads to place beneath your knees and hands, but standing works all the same.

Step 1: Stand Up Straight

Stand up straight with shoulders back and face forward. Take a deep breath and engage your core as you begin.

Step 2: Touch Your Right Knee To Left Elbow

Lift your right knee up towards your chest while simultaneously bringing your left arm up with your palm facing forward. Then bring your left elbow down to touch your right knee. This should twist your torso slightly. Keep your your core engaged and balance steady.

Step 3: Return To Neutral Position

Return your right leg to the ground and left arm gently to your side as you stand up straight again for a moment.

Step 4: Alternate To The Other Knee And Elbow

Alternate to the other knee and elbow, bringing your left knee and right arm up, before touching elbow to knee.

Step 5: Repeat In A Rhythmic Fashion

Repeat the alternating movements in a fluid, rhythmic fashion. It should look almost as if you were crawling in the air. Bring your awareness to the sensations through your body and take note of how you feel. Repeat for a few minutes or so before coming to a gentle standstill.

EXERCISE 27:
ARM STRETCHING AND RELEASING

There are many effective arm stretching and releasing exercises designed to release tension, stretch muscles, increase flexibility, and improve well-being. Tension in the neck and arms can create stiffness, nerve pain, and even pinched nerves. Practicing arm stretching and releasing regularly can help you avoid chronic problems and damage that may inhibit functioning.

Instructions

Find a comfortable place to sit down with a straight back and neutral head position. I'm going to share 3 highly effective arm stretches and releases that you can add to your somatic practice for a more targeted release.

Release 1: Neck And Shoulder Rolls

Starting with your shoulders, sit up straight and roll your shoulders forward repeatedly. Breathe in deeply throughout. Switch to rolling the shoulders backward for a couple of rounds.

Next, drop your chin down to your chest and roll your head from left to right. You can also roll slightly past your shoulder on either side to stretch the sides of the front of your neck. Feel the stretch releasing throughout your shoulders, decolletage, and neck.

Release 2: Tricep Stretch

The triceps are a muscle we are not often aware of, making them a common place for tension to be stored. Stretching one arm at a time, reach the arm up above your head and bend the elbow allowing your hand to drop gently behind your back. Your elbow should be pointing toward the ceiling.

Next, take your opposite hand and place it on your elbow. Use the opposite hand to pull the elbow inward and backward slightly, feeling a nice stretch along the tricep. Repeat on the other arm.

Release 3: Eagle Arms Stretch

Reach both arms forward, crossing them at the elbow. Now turn both palms to face each other, bringing them together in a twisted arm position. Hold your hands together and lift them above your head. Hold the stretch and feel your arms and shoulders getting a nice release.

You can use this stretch behind your back, lifting your arms up to stretch and squeeze your shoulder blades. For either stretch, alternate which hand is on the top.

EXERCISE 28: SIDE BENDS

Side bends are a great addition to any stretching or somatic routine to target tension release and increased flexibility in the sides of the torso. This exercise works to stretch and strengthen the obliques and intercostal muscles for improved lateral flexibility.

Instructions

Find somewhere you can comfortably stand and extend your arms out to your sides. You can also do seated side bends if necessary.

Step 1: Stand Up Straight And Inhale

Stand with your spine straight and posture neutral. Inhale deeply through your nose, reaching your arms out to either side of your body like a starfish.

Step 2: Bend At The Hip And Reach Down To The Left

Starting on your left side, bend your torso over to the left at the hips. Keep your gaze forward and drop your left arm down, sliding it along your left leg as you stretch. You can keep your right arm extended into the air or deepen the stretch by bringing it over your head to the left.

Step 3: Feel The Stretch And Hold

Continue to breathe deeply as you hold the stretch. Tune into the sensations of the stretch, feeling any tension or discomfort before releasing.

Step 4: Release And Straighten Up Slowly

Soften the stretch and slowly bring your torso back up with arms extended at either side again. Feel the contrast between the stretch and relaxation. Notice the softness and any other sensations you feel.

Step 5: Repeat On The Other Side

Repeat the steps on the other side, stretching your right arm down your right side to stretch the left side of your torso. Repeat on both sides for a minute or so, holding, stretching, and breathing deeply for a relaxing release.

EXERCISE 29: KNEE-TO-CHEST STRETCH

The knee-to-chest stretch is a simple stretch with a lot of benefits. Lying down on the ground and stretching one knee to the chest at a time offers a tremendous tension release in the hips and lower back. This exercise can improve flexibility and promote relaxation. It is the perfect choice for those who spend a lot of time sitting.

Instructions

Find a comfortable place to lie flat on your back with your legs extended. You can complete this exercise on your bed, but a floor may provide some extra tension release as the muscles massage against a harder surface.

Step 1: Sink Into The Starting Position

Lying flat on your back with legs extended straight down and arms relaxed by your sides, take a couple of deep breaths, feeling your body press into the ground.

Step 2: Bend One Knee And Hold

Slowly bend one knee, bringing it up towards your chest. Use your hand to hold it in place and deepen the stretch. You can hold the leg at the shin or thigh, wherever is most comfortable.

Step 3: Slowly Lower And Switch

Lower the raised leg slowly back onto the ground, taking note of the release you feel. Raise your other leg up towards your chest and repeat.

Step 4: Knee To Chest Variation

You can take this stretch further by bringing both legs up to your chest at the same time. Hold with your hands and if you're comfortable with it, you can rock slightly from side to side for a nice deep hip and lower back release.

Step 5: Feel The Sensations

Take a moment to close your eyes and sink into the hip stretch. This exercise is best practiced slowly, allowing the weight of your body to melt away tension. Continue to breathe deeply and tune into any sensations you feel. When you're ready, sink back into the starting position to rest for a moment.

EXERCISE 30: FIGURE-EIGHT HIP MOVEMENTS

Often used in dance routines, but also an all-around lower body release, figure-eight hip movements are fluid and fun. The smooth swaying motion engages muscles around the hip joints helping to strengthen them and promote a full range of motion. This exercise reduces tension in the pelvis, spine, and hips while boosting a sense of well-being.

Instructions

This movement is completed in a standing position with feet about hip width apart. Find somewhere you can comfortably swing your hips and have fun with this exercise.

Step 1: Prepare To Move

Standing up straight with your feet about hip-width apart, place your hands on your hips and face forward.

Step 2: Begin The Figure Of Eight

To begin the figure of eight, turn your hips to face the right without moving your feet. From this position lead the figure of eight with your left hip, alternating between the two hips as we go.

Step 3: Draw The Figure Of Eight

Draw a figure of eight, imagining that the cross point of the eight is at your center of gravity. Pull your hips from left to right in a figure of eight, turning your hips to face either side slightly as you go.

Step 4: Get Into The Swing Of It

If you're comfortable completing this movement, allow yourself to get into a flow. Let your hips swing lightly through the figure of eight, feeling the fluidity and release.

Step 5: Have Fun With It

Allow yourself to have fun with this exercise. Notice any shifts in your mobility and mood as you go. Tune into any sensations or cues of relaxation. This is an exercise that can easily boost your mood and feelings of well-being.

EXERCISE 31: PSOAS RELEASE EXERCISE

The psoas is a deep-seated muscle connecting the lumbar spine to the femur.[4] It is a common place for tension to build and is a difficult place to find release. Most regular stretches for the back and hips do not fully expand or relax this muscle. These psoas release exercises can target the muscle directly, reducing lower back discomfort and improving hip flexibility.

Instructions

Find a comfortable place where you have enough space to complete these exercises. I'm going to share three of the most effective on-the-ground psoas release exercises.

Exercise 1: Supported Psoas Stretch

Start by kneeling with one knee on the ground and bringing your other foot in front forming a 90-degree angle. You can place a cushion or folded blanket under your knee for comfort. Tilt your pelvis to create a slight arch in your back.

When you're ready, shift your weight forward gently, allowing your hips to rock forward, stretching the front of the hip and the back of the leg. Release the position by gently rocking back to your original position. Switch legs and repeat on the other side.

Exercise 2: Hip Raises For Psoas Release

Start by lying on your back with your knees bent and feet on the ground. Keep your feet in line with your hips and raise your pelvis off the ground. Slowly raise and lower your pelvis off the ground to engage the glute muscles and stretch the front of your hips.

To deepen the psoas release of this exercise, complete about a minute or two of hip raises before slowly moving to a standing position. Once standing, place your hands on your lower back, and stretch your hips forward. You should feel a nice release in your lower back area.

Exercise 3: Active Psoas Release

Start in a lunge position, placing your knee on the ground with your other foot in front at a 90-degree angle. When you're ready, slide your knee back into a high lunge position. You can distribute your weight across the knee, foot, and lower leg. Place this back leg on a folded blanket for more support if needed.

To activate the release, engage your core and tuck your pelvis under slightly. Gently rock your hips forward and back against your front leg feeling the release along the front of your back leg and hip. Slowly come back to neutral and switch legs. Repeat on the other side.

EXERCISE 32: LATERAL NECK STRETCH

This neck stretch, known as the lateral neck stretch, does exactly what you would expect – stretching and releasing the lateral muscles of the neck. The muscles along the side of the neck include some shoulder muscles such as the trapezius. This stretch can relieve tension, increase flexibility, and reduce stiffness in all of these muscles simultaneously.

Instructions

Find a comfortable place to sit for this stretch. You can do it on the edge of a bed, on the floor, or at your work desk. It's a great stretch to do throughout the day helping to release tension and prevent tension build up.

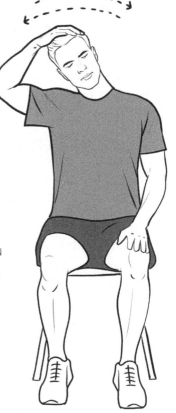

Step 1: Sit Up Straight And Inhale

Take a moment to sit up straight. You can take a couple of deep breaths in this position first, or simply inhale deeply and move ont the stretch.

Step 2: Tilt Your Head To One Side

On the exhale, drop your head slowly to one side, almost reaching it toward your shoulder. Avoid lifting your shoulders, keep them square throughout. Allow the weight of your head to stretch the muscles.

Step 3: Slowly Release And Repeat

When you're ready, slowly lift your head back to a neutral position. Take a deep breath in and repeat on the other side.

Step 4: Deepen The Stretch

To deepen this stretch, use your hand to apply slight pressure onto the side of your head. If you are tilting your head to the left, bring your left hand over and onto the right side near your ear. Simply rest your hand here to deepen the stretch. Avoid applying too much pressure.

Step 5: Notice The Sensations

As you stretch your lateral neck muscles, notice any tension or stiffness you feel. Use your breath to release tension, and notice if your head continues to drop down as the muscles release. You can take note of your progress by monitoring your stiffness or range of motion.

EXERCISE 33: SELF-MASSAGE

Self-massage is a somatic practice that allows you to directly target and focus on relieving tension in specific muscles. Using your hands or massage tools, you can apply pressure to your muscles and work out the tension or stiffness. Self-massage is a great way to relax, foster a stronger mind-body connection, and feel empowered to take care of your tension.

Instructions

You can sit or lie down for this exercise, adjusting your position as you massage different muscles throughout your body.

Step 1: Deep Breathing

It's easier to release muscle tension through massage when you are in a relaxed frame of mind. Take a few deep diaphragmatic breaths before you begin.

Step 2: Complete A Body Scan

To help you decide where your body needs massaging most, you can use a body scan meditation. Scan your awareness through your body, taking note of any areas that feel tense or uncomfortable.

Step 3: Massage With Your Hands

Start massaging the tense area you are working on with your hands. You can use your fingertips, palms, or knuckles to stroke the area. Some common massage strokes include circular motions, long strokes, and kneading. You can apply as much pressure as you're comfortable with.

Step 4: Tips To Deepen Self-Massage

To achieve a better result with self-massage, you can try:

- Using massage oils or lotion.

- Implementing massage tools like foam rollers or massage balls.

- Move intuitively, adjusting positions and pressure to what feels best.

Step 5: Lean Into Relaxation

The more relaxed you can become during self-massage, the easier it will be to release tension. Lean into relaxation by closing your eyes, tuning into the sensations, and centering yourself into the present moment.

SECTION 6

BALANCE AND FOCUS

EXERCISE 34:
BALANCING ON ONE FOOT

The balancing act of trying to keep steady on one foot is a good indication of your proprioception and coordination. However, it can also be improved with practice. As your balance improves so will your overall proprioception, focus, and stability within your body. Balancing on one foot is a fun somatic practice to work on improved balance.

Instructions

To practice balancing on one foot, you will need to find a comfortable, sturdy place to stand. However, if you need assistance, you can use the back of a chair or stand near a wall for support.

Step 1: Stand Up Tall

Start by standing up tall with feet about hip-width apart. Take a few deep breaths in and decide on an arm position. Hands on the hips is a great start.

Step 2: Shift Weight Onto One Leg

When you're ready, shift your entire weight onto one foot, lifting the other off the ground slightly.

Step 3: Engage Core And Balance

Engage your core and place your foot where you're comfortable. This can be resting on the other foot for an easier variation or held up at your shin with the knee bent. Hold this position and balance for up to 30 seconds.

Step 4: Switch Legs

When you're ready, switch positions to the other side. Keep your arm and feet position the same for the other side for an even sense of balance. Repeat on steps 2 & 3.

Step 5: Challenge Yourself

You can repeat the exercise as is for a few minutes. However, if you'd like to challenge yourself and further improve your balance you can:

- Close your eyes.

- Stand without an aid.

- Hold arms out to the side.

- Stand on a yoga block.

As you try new ways to balance, monitor your progress and see what a difference it makes.

EXERCISE 35: SOMATIC EMPATHY EXERCISE

The somatic empathy exercise is arguably one of the most important somatic practices for emotional trauma release or regulation. It is an exercise where you can explore the complex interplay between emotions and the body, learning to connect emotions and sensations. It's important to withhold a strong sense of self-compassion and curiosity when practicing to improve your sense of well-being and self-care.

Instructions

You can choose to sit or lie down for this exercise, finding a comfortable place where you won't be disturbed. Take a few deep breaths to prepare and get started.

Step 1: Reflect On Your Emotions

Close your eyes as you breathe deeply. Take a moment to notice and reflect on any emotions you feel.
Whatever emotions you feel, such as anxiety, anger, joy, or peace, try to put a label on them if possible.

Step 2: Complete A Body Scan

Next, keeping your eyes closed, complete a body scan exercise. Scan your awareness from head to toe, taking note of any sensations you feel. Simply acknowledge the sensations and move on.

Step 3: Connect Emotions With Sensations

Without judgment, take a moment to decipher which sensations belong to your emotions. Some sensations may have nothing to do with how you feel. However, others may be present because of the emotion.

Step 4: Release And Let Go

Once you've practiced somatic empathy, it's important to release and let go of any negative emotions and tension. Do what feels right, such as any somatic movements, deep breathing, or mindful visualizations.

Step 5: Reflect On The Change

Take a moment to reflect on how you feel both emotionally and physically. Notice the changes and compare the sensations to how you felt before. You can also use this time to journal down which sensations you discovered were connected to which emotions.

6

YOUR PERSONALIZED SOMATIC EXERCISE PLAN

10 Minutes Per Day For A Harmonized
Nervous System

*"Success is the sum of small efforts repeated
day in and day out."*

– Robert Collier

Think of a set of guitar strings stretching along the body from the head to the bridge. Every time the strings are played, they loosen a little. The strings are eventually stressed out of tune and need a tune-up to sound great again. The human nervous system is much the same.

When we experience stressors in our lives, our nervous system takes a hit. But if we haven't tuned it up in a while, the stressors we could once tolerate create an unorchestrated reaction within us. When we don't have nervous system harmony, stress can create chaos in the body.

But just like a guitar, with regular maintenance and tuning, the nervous system can strengthen to the point of withstanding stress. When the strings are well-oiled and tightly tuned, the sound can easily bounce off of them. A regular somatic practice is enough to tune up the nervous system so stress can simply bounce off of it.

10 minutes a day is all you need for a harmonized nervous system in the long term. Quality and regularity are far more beneficial than time spent. In this chapter, I'm going to guide you through creating a somatic exercise plan that is tailored to your nervous system. Each of us has different stressors, different bodies, and unique somatic responses. A tailored plan will make sure that the 10 minutes you spend doing somatics daily are worth it.

WHERE TO START

To choose the right exercises for your exercise plan, you'll need to get to the bottom of what your needs are. This is an opportunity to reflect back on the body scan you did in Chapter 2. However, you can complete a more recent or thorough body scan right now to help you gain more insights into your physical and psychological well-being. There will be a new outline for you to fill in in your Workbook.

When you're ready, there is a questionnaire in your Workbook with questions that will help you further evaluate your physical and emotional state. Please take a moment to fill those out before continuing.

Now that you're clear on your unique and targeted needs, the next step toward a complete 10-minute somatic exercise plan is to set goals. There is space in your Workbook to write down your goals. Some tips to help you define clear and achievable objectives include:

- Be specific and clear.

- Choose measurable benchmarks.

- Have realistic expectations.

- Assign a realistic time frame to each goal.

- Ensure they align with your overall well-being.

- Be open to adjusting them if necessary.

- Celebrate your successes, no matter how small.

Take a moment to fill out your goals in your Workbook. Choose 2 easily attainable goals, 2 more challenging goals, and 1 main goal or objective.

CHOOSING EXERCISES

This is the most personal part of your exercise plan. Which exercises you choose to do daily will come down to a few important factors, including your:

- Needs: Reflect on your self-assessment and goals.

- Focus: What is your main goal? For example improved well-being, mobility, or relaxation.

- Mobility: Which exercises work best for your mobility levels.

- Environment: How much space or privacy do you have to work with

- Comfort: Which exercises are you psychologically comfortable practicing.

In your Workbook, there is a checklist of the 35 exercises you learned in Chapter 5. Consider choosing up to 10 exercises on the list. Depending on your overall goal and target areas, you can choose exercises from each section or fine-tune your selection to just one or two sections. If you're unsure, take some time to go back to Chapter 5 and feel which exercises are right for you.

CREATING YOUR PLAN

Once you've chosen up to 10 exercises, consider the time you'd like to spend on each. You may end up choosing just 5 of the 10 exercises for a consistent daily plan, or you can alternate between the exercises on different days. Hypothetically, you could even practice all 35 exercises by sectioning off the exercises into a 7-day plan of just 10 minutes a day. It's completely up to you.

The important thing to aim for with a daily somatic practice is balance. If you're going to complete the same set of exercises daily, make sure to complete them in an order that compliments one another. For example

- 1-minute warm-up body scan

- 5 minutes of seated somatic exercises (3 exercises)

- 2 minutes of standing somatic exercises (1 exercise)

- 1-minute cool-down visualization and breathing

This simple layout is a great way to create a nice flowing routine with a beginning and an end. You might choose to start and end your daily workout in the same way while alternating the exercises in between. To end up with a layout like this, you could choose exercises in the following way:

- 1-minute warm-up: One exercise to center the mind (ie. Somatic breath counting).

- 6 minutes of main exercises: this could be 3 exercises of your choice (2 minutes each).

- 2-minute release: A releasing exercise (ie. shaking or releasing visualization).

- 1-minute cool-down: One final exercise to process and integrate the experience (ie. Diaphragmatic breathing).

If you are someone who prefers a more flexible schedule, you could decide on a layout like the one above and choose a selection of exercises you could alternate between during the main portion of your daily somatic workout. Use the space in your Workbook to create a daily somatic exercise plan.

For example, if you have 10 main exercises that work great for you, you could warm up with a body scan and intuitively choose the 3 exercises that you feel are most needed for the day. Provided that you only spend 2 minutes on each exercise, you can keep your workout within the 10-minute slot you've allocated for your somatic practice.

MONITOR YOUR PROGRESS

The shifts and progress felt after practicing somatic exercises can range from subtle to life-changing. However, most of the time, it's the small changes that add up to life-changing results. Keeping track of these small changes will help you to look back and recognize how far you've come. Monitoring your progress and celebrating the smallest improvements will be incredibly encouraging. Some things you can do to actively recognize your progress include:

- Journaling: Take notes of your sessions. Mark down any new sensations, thoughts, experiences or changes you notice. This can mean a quick written check-in before and after each session.

- Identify markers of progress: These can include flexibility, pain, mood, or psychological changes.

- Identify increased awareness: Look out for signs of an improved mind-body awareness such as improved appetite, quicker recognition of emotions, or an improved ability to identify target areas.

- Talking to a friend or doctor: feedback from friends, relatives, or your doctor is a great resource for tracking progress. You could also reach out to them for help when facing a challenge to recieve the necessary support.

- Checking off and setting goals: setting small attainable goals is another great way to track progress as you can check them off your list as you go, taking note of your past goals and setting new ones for continued encouragement and motivation.

There are pages provided for a week of somatic journaling to help you track your progress. Keeping track of your progress is also a great way to know when you need to change things. If you follow your somatic exercise plan and don't see results for some time, it might be a sign that you're not feeling challenged enough. This is an opportunity to reevaluate your daily 10-minute workout strategy. Maybe there's an exercise that you could switch out or deepen. Give yourself the benefit of the doubt and try out exercises you previously felt were out of your comfort zone.

The truth about progress is that sometimes what once worked starts to feel ineffective because you've made more progress than you've realized! If this happens, simply try out some more difficult variations of the exercises you love or switch up your plan completely.

Our bodies shift and change constantly. Be sure to check in with yourself regularly to make sure your goals are still aligned with your changing needs. If a specific problem you had starts to resolve and new areas of tension emerge, start at the beginning of this chapter and have fun creating a new 10-minute somatic exercise plan tailored to your new goals and needs.

The nervous system, like strings on a guitar, can be tuned up to better handle stress – this is known as a toned nervous system. The most important thing to remember about a somatic practice is consistency. If your nervous system feels out of tune, it's important to commit to spending time within yourself daily, even when you feel good.

Sometimes, a guitar can still function and sound good when the strings are a day away from needing a retune. So rather than waiting for dysregulation, keep your nervous system strong and toned with daily practice.

CONCLUSION

Healing is one of the most challenging yet rewarding journeys one can face. Both mental or physical healing journeys require the other to see long-term progress. Because of the mind-body connection, physical healing takes mental harmony, and vice versa. We are complex beings made up of an intricate entanglement of physical and mental processes. You can't have one without the other. Knowing that is a superpower.

When you build a strong mind-body connection, paired with your deep desire to be well, you become an empowered self-healer. You access one of the most miraculous mechanisms in existence – the mind-body connection. And because it is something that has been overlooked in most other healing modalities, it's what makes somatics so special.

I love the thought that during this book, you most likely stopped what you were doing, got up from where you were lying down or sitting, and tried out at least one of the 35 somatic exercises. I love that you felt compelled to move your body, tune into it, and *feel*. That is true action. And as I like to remind myself and others, healing takes action.

You have to make a choice and do something about your pain, trauma, or stress. It's not likely to go away on its own, and all I can wish for is that since reading this book, you feel more empowered to take the necessary action to relieve your struggles. You deserve so much to be comfortable and safe in your body. Let somatic practice guide the way.

REFERENCES

1. https://www.nichd.nih.gov/health/topics/neuro/
    conditioninfo/functions#:~:text=The%20nervous%20
    system%20plays%20a,Brain%20growth%20and%20
    development

2. https://greatergood.berkeley.edu/article/item/how_to_
    grow_the_good_in_your_brain

3. https://www.ncbi.nlm.nih.gov/pmc/articles/
    PMC4427060/#:~:text=Sighs%20monitor%20changes%20
    in%20brain,thereby%20become%20critical%20for%20
    survival

4. https://www.ncbi.nlm.nih.gov/books/
    NBK535418/#:~:text=The%20psoas%20muscle%20is%20
    among,to%20form%20the%20iliopsoas%20muscle

Made in the USA
Coppell, TX
28 May 2024

32878456R00079